SING & PRAISE

Wise Publications
London/New York/Sydney/Paris/Copenhagen/Madrid

PIANO/KEYBOARD EDITION

Exclusive Distributors:
Music Sales Limited
8/9 Frith Street, London W1V 5TZ, England.

Music Sales Pty Limited
120 Rothschild Avenue, Rosebery, NSW 2018, Australia.

Order No. AM951698
ISBN 0-7119-7449-7

www.internetmusicshop.com

Compiled by Robert Lamont.
Music processed by Paul Ewers Music Design.
Cover design by Michael Bell Design.

Printed in the United Kingdom by
MPG Books Limited, Bodmin, Cornwall.

All Hail The Lamb

Dave Bilbrough

Abba, Father, Let Me Be

Dave Bilbrough

C♯7
F♯m
C♯7
F♯m
Ne - ver let my heart grow cold,

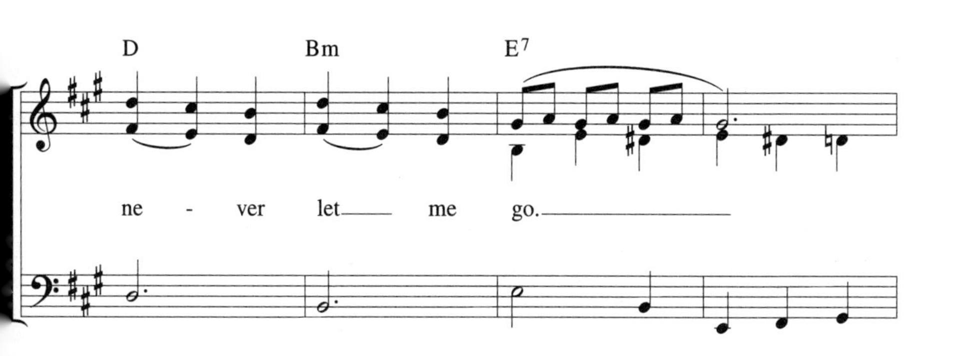
D
Bm
E7
ne - ver let me go.

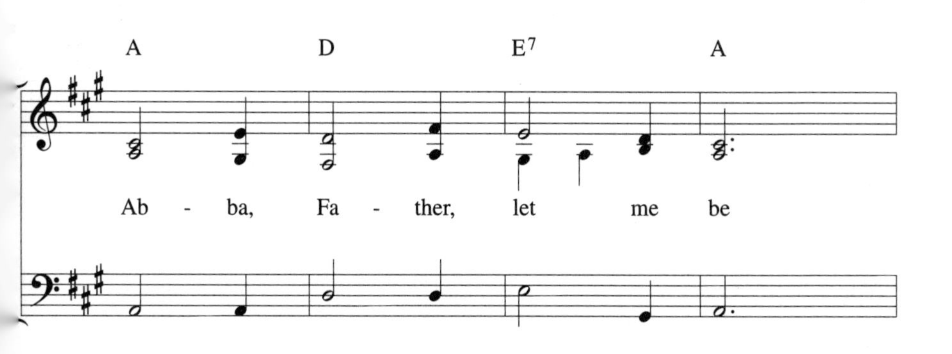
A
D
E7
A
Ab - ba, Fa - ther, let me be

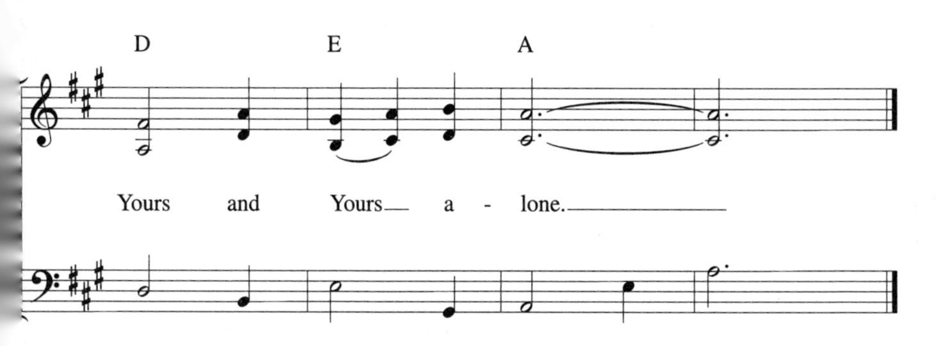
D
E
A
Yours and Yours a - lone.

All I Once Held Dear

(Knowing You)

Graham Kendrick

Am
Em/G
F
is no great - er thing. You're my
C/E
F/A
C/G
F
all, You're the best, You're my joy, my right-eous-ness, and I
1, 2.
3.
C/E
F/A
C/G
G
love You, Lord. 2. Now my love You, Lord,
C/G
F/G
C
love You, Lord.
Verse 2:
Now my heart's desire
Is to know You more
To be found in You
And known as Yours.
To posess by faith
What I could not earn
All-surpassing gift
Of righteousness.
Verse 3:
Oh, to know the pow'r
Of Your risen life
And to know You in
Your sufferings.
To become like You
In Your death, my Lord
So with You to live
And never die.

All Heaven Declares

Noel Richards / Tricia Richards

Verse 2:
I will proclaim the glory of the risen Lord
Who once was slain to reconcile man to God
Forever You will be the Lamb upon the throne
I gladly bow the knee and worship You alone.

And He Shall Reign

Graham Kendrick

D
A
F♯m
Bm
A
reign for ev - - - - er, and
To Coda
G
A
D
G/D
D
D sus4
we shall reign with Him.
Verse
D
A
Bm
G
A
1. What a vi - sion filled my
Bm
A/C♯
D
G
A
eyes, one like a Son of
D
G/D
D add9
A/D
D
man. Com - - - ing

Verse 2:
He was given sov'reign power
Glory and authority
Every nation, tribe and tongue
Worshipped Him on bended knee.

Verse 3:
On the throne for ever
See the Lamb who once was slain
Wounds of sacrificial love
For ever shall remain.

As The Deer Pants

Martin Nystrom

Verse 2:
I want You more than gold or silver
Only You can satisfy.
You alone are the real joy-giver
And the apple of my eye.

Verse 3:
You're my friend and You are my brother
Even though You are a King.
I love You more than any other
So much more than anything.

As We Are Gathered

John Daniels

At The Foot Of The Cross

Derek Bond

Gsus4 Am G Em7 F C/E C
and the hard-ness of my sin - ful heart that
Am7 Fadd9/A Gsus4 G
left You there for dead. And
Am G/A F C
O what mer - cy I have found, at the
Am G/A C/G F Am G/A
cross of Cal-va - ry; I will nev - er know Your lone-
F Am C/G Fadd9/G G7sus4 G7
- li - ness, all on ac - count of me. And I will

Am G/A F C
bow my knee before Your throne, 'cause Your
Am G/A C/G F
love has set me free; and I will
Am G/A F C/E Dm7 F
give my life to You, dear Lord, and praise Your
G G/B Am
(Optional repeat)
ma - jes - ty, and
F G C
praise Your ma - jes - ty.

At The Name Of Jesus

Michael Brierly / Caroline Maria Noel

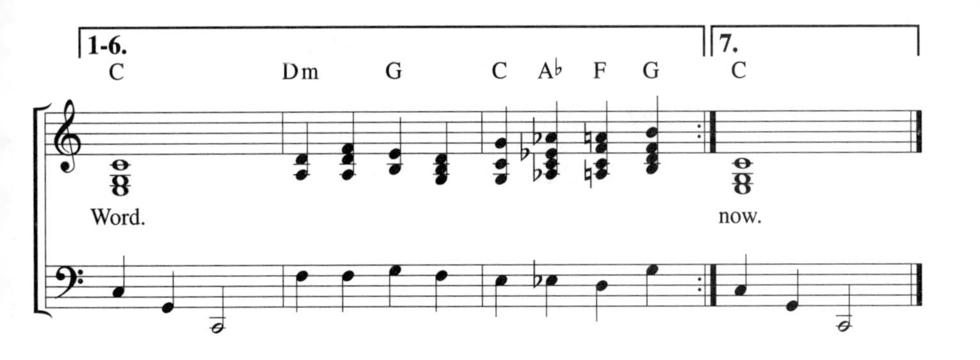

Verse 2:
At his voice creation
Sprang at once to sight
All the angel faces
All the hosts of light
Thrones and dominations
Stars upon their way
All the heav'nly orders
In their great array.

Verse 3:
Humbled for a season
To receive a name
From the lips of sinners
Unto whom he came
Faithfully he bore it
Spotless to the last
Brought it back victorious
When from death he passed.

Verse 4:
Bore it up triumphant
With its human light
Through all ranks of creatures
To the central height
To the throne of Godhead
To the Father's breast
Filled it with the glory
Of that perfect rest.

Verse 5:
All creation, name him
With love as strong as death
But with awe and wonder
And with bated breath.
He is God the Saviour
He is Christ the Lord
Ever to be worshipped
Trusted and adored.

Verse 6:
In your hearts enthrone him
There let him subdue
All that is not holy
All that is not true
Crown him as your captain
In temptation's hour
Let his will enfold you
In its light and pow'r.

Verse 7:
Truly, this Lord Jesus
Shall return again
With his Father's glory
With his angel train
For all wreaths of empire
Meet upon his brow
And our hearts confess him
King of glory now.

At Your Feet We Fall Mighty Risen Lord

(I Am He That Liveth)

David Fellingham

Verse 2:
There we see You stand, mighty risen Lord
Clothed in garments pure and holy, shining bright.
Eyes of flashing fire, feet like burnished bronze
And the sound of many waters is Your voice.

Verse 3:
Like the shining sun in its noonday strength
We now see the glory of Your wondrous face.
Once that face was marred, but now you're glorified
And Your words like a two-edged sword have mighty pow'r.

Be Bold, Be Strong

Morris Chapman

F G Am F G
I am not dis - mayed, be-cause I'm walk-ing in faith and
Am F G Am
vic - to - ry, come on and walk in faith and vic - to - ry, for the
F G G7
Lord, your God, is with you.
1. C 2. C
Be bold,

Be Still, For The Presence Of The Lord

(The Holy One Is Here)

David J. Evans

Verse 2:
Be still, for the glory of the Lord
Is shining all around
He burns with holy fire
With splendour He is crowned
How awesome is the sight
Our radiant king of light!
Be still, for the glory of the Lord
Is shining all around.

Verse 3:
Be still, for the power of the Lord
Is moving in this place
He comes to cleanse and heal
To minister His grace
No work too hard for Him.
In faith receive from Him.
Be still, for the power of the Lord
Is moving in this place.

Beauty For Brokenness

(God Of The Poor)

Graham Kendrick

1, 3.
2, 4, 5.
G C/G G C/G G
-crease.
speak.
Chorus
D7 G B7 Em
God of the poor, friend of the weak,
C Am7 D D7/F♯
give us com-pas - sion, we pray, melt our cold
G B7 Em C
hearts, let tears fall like rain. Come, change our love
Am7 C/D Gadd9
from a spark to a flame.

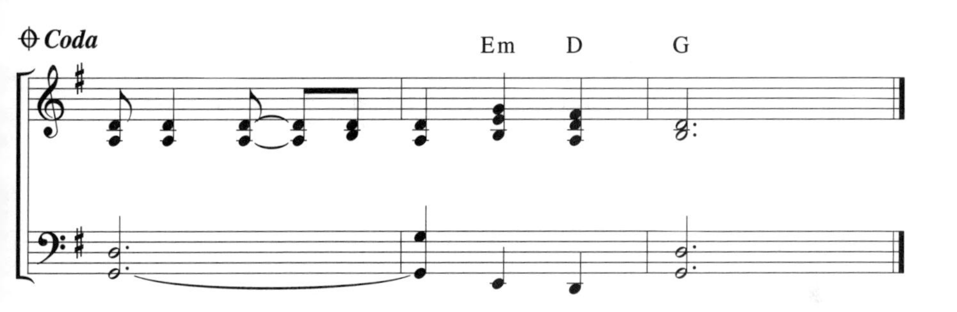

Verse 2:
Shelter for fragile lives
Cures for their ills
Work for the craftsmen
Trade for their skills
Land for the dispossessed
Rights for the weak
Voices to plead the cause
Of those who can't speak.

Verse 3:
Refuge from cruel wars
Havens from fear
Cities for sanctu'ry
Freedoms to share
Peace to the killing fields
Scorched earth to green
Christ for the bitterness
His cross for the pain.

Verse 4:
Rest for the ravaged earth
Oceans and streams
Plundered and poisoned
Our future, our dreams
Lord, end our madness
Carelessness, greed
Make us content with
The things that we need.

Verse 5:
Lighten our darkness
Breathe on this flame
Until Your justice
Burns brightly again
Until the nations
Learn of Your ways
Seek Your salvation
And bring You their praise.

Be Thou My Vision

Traditional Irish
Words translated by Mary Byrne / Eleanor Hull

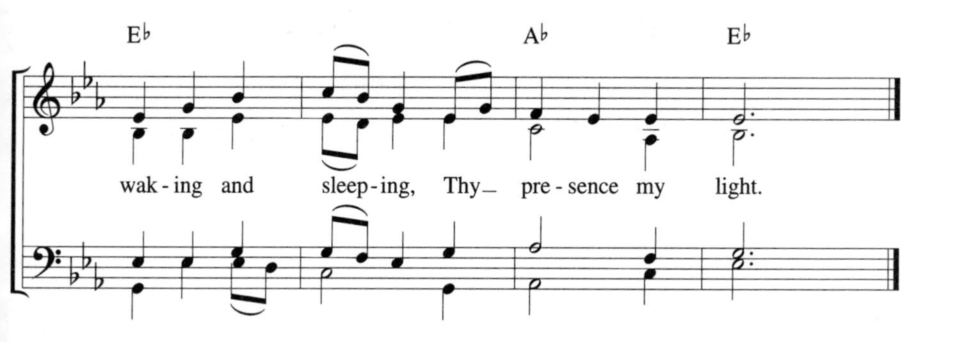

Verse 2:
Be Thou my wisdom, be Thou my true word
Be Thou ever with me, and I with Thee, Lord
Be Thou my great Father, and I Thy true son
Be Thou in me dwelling, and I with Thee one.

Verse 3:
Be Thou my breastplate, my sword for the fight
Be Thou my whole armour, be Thou my true might
Be Thou my soul's shelter, be Thou my strong tower
O raise Thou me heavenward, great Power of my power.

Verse 4:
Riches I need not, nor man's empty praise
Be Thou mine inheritance now and always
Be Thou and Thou only the first in my heart
O Sovereign of heaven, my treasure Thou art.

Verse 5:
High King of heaven, Thou heaven's bright Sun
O grant me its joys after victory is won
Great Heart of my own heart, whatever befall
Still be Thou my vision, O Ruler of all.

Behold The Lord

Gerald Coates / Noel Richards

Verse 2:
The first, the last, the living One
Laid down His life for all the world
Behold, He now lives for evermore
And holds the keys of death and hell.
Holy, holy, Lord God Almighty
Holy, holy, we bow before Your throne.

Verse 3:
So let our praises ever ring
To Jesus Christ, our glorious King
All heaven and earth resound as we cry
'Worthy is the Son of God!'
Holy, holy, Lord God Almighty
Holy, holy, we fall down at Your feet.

Blessed Be The Name Of The Lord

Clinton Utterbach

Verse 2:
Jesus reigns on high in all the earth
Jesus reigns on high in all the earth
Jesus reigns on high in all the earth
Jesus reigns on high in all the earth.
The universe is in the hands of the Lord
The universe is in the hands of the Lord.

Blessing And Honour

(The Ancient Of Days)

Jamie Harvill / Gary Sadler

With an 'island' feel

Chorus
F
Dm7
G
C/E
Ev - 'ry tongue in hea - ven and earth shall de - clare Your glo - ry,
F
Dm7
G
C/E
Em7
ev - 'ry knee shall bow at Your throne in wor - ship;
F
Dm7
G
C/E
Em7
You will be ex - al - ted, O God, and Your
F
Dm7
G
F/G
To Coda
king - dom shall not pass a - way. O An-cient of Day
C
Csus4
C
Csus4
Your

C
king - dom shall reign ov - er all the earth:
B♭/C F/C Gm/C B♭/C C5
sing un - to the An - cient of Days. For
C
none shall com - pare to your match - less worth:
D.𝄋. al Coda
B♭/C F/C Gm/C B♭/C C5 C/E
sing un - to the An - cient of Days.
Coda
C Csus4 C

Broken For Me

Janet Lunt

Verse 2:
Come to my table and with me dine
Eat of my bread and drink of my wine.

Verse 3:
This is my body given for you
Eat it remembering I died for you.

Verse 4:
This is my blood I shed for you
For your forgiveness, making you new.

By Your Side

Noel Richards / Tricia Richards

Cm7 B♭ F
I with - hold.
E♭ B♭/D Cm7 F/A
Lord, I love You, and a-dore You; what more can I
B♭ E♭ B♭/D
say? You cause my love to grow strong - er
1. 2.
Cm7 Fsus4 F B♭ Cm7 B♭/D B♭
with ev - 'ry pass-ing day. day.

Come And See

(We Worship At Your Feet)

Graham Kendrick

Verse 2:
Come and weep, come and mourn
For your sin that pierced Him there
So much deeper than the
wounds of thorn and nail
All our pride, all our greed
All our fallenness and shame
And the Lord has laid the punishment on Him.

Verse 3:
Man of heaven, born to earth
To restore us to Your heaven
Here we bow in awe beneath
Your searching eyes
From Your tears comes our joy
From Your death our life shall spring
By Your resurrection power we shall rise.

Come On And Celebrate

(Celebrate)

Dave Bankhead / Patricia Morgan

Em
Am7
D
we'll give to You our of - fer - ing in ce - le - bra - tion
G
C
praise. Come on and ce - le - brate,
Am
G
Em
ce - le - brate, ce - le - brate and sing,
1.
Am7
D
G
ce - le - brate and sing to the King. Come on and
2.
Am7
D
G
ce - le - brate and sing to the King.

Creation Is Awaiting

Chris Bowater / Ian Taylor

Verse 2:
The church is awaiting the return of the King
The people joined together in His love
Redeemed by His blood
Washed in His word
As a bride longs for her bridegroom
The church looks to God.

The King is coming, the King is coming
The King is coming to receive His bride.

Verse 3:
The world is awaiting the return of the King
The earth is a footstool for His feet
Every knee will bow down
Every tongue confess
That Jesus Christ is Lord
Of heaven and earth.

The King is coming, the King is coming
The King is coming to reign in majesty.

Down The Mountain The River Flows

(The River Is Here)

Andy Park

Verse 2:
The river of God is teeming with life
And all who touch it can be revived
And those who linger on this river's shore
Will come back thirsting for more of the Lord.

Verse 3:
Up to the mountain we love to go
To find the presence of the Lord
Along the banks of the river we run
We dance with laughter, giving praise to the Son.

Faithful God

Chris Bowater

Faithful One

Brian Doerksen

A7sus4 A D D/F♯ G A
I call out to You a-gain and a -

D D/F♯ G A D D/F♯
- gain, I call out to You

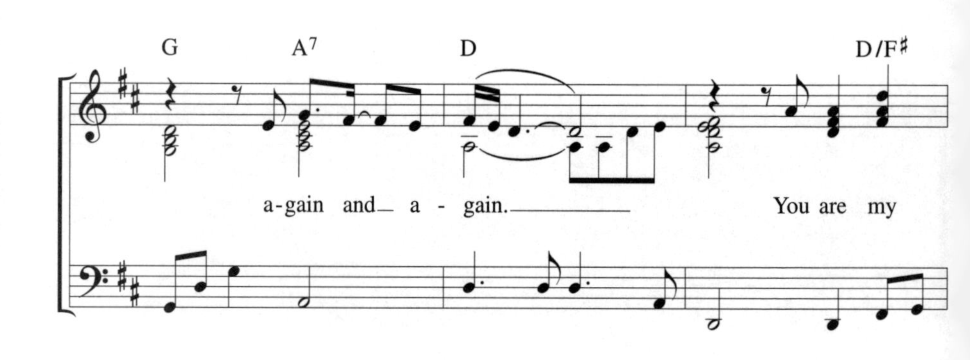
G A7 D D/F♯
a-gain and a - gain. You are my

A G D
rock in times of trou - ble,

A
G
You lift me up when I fall

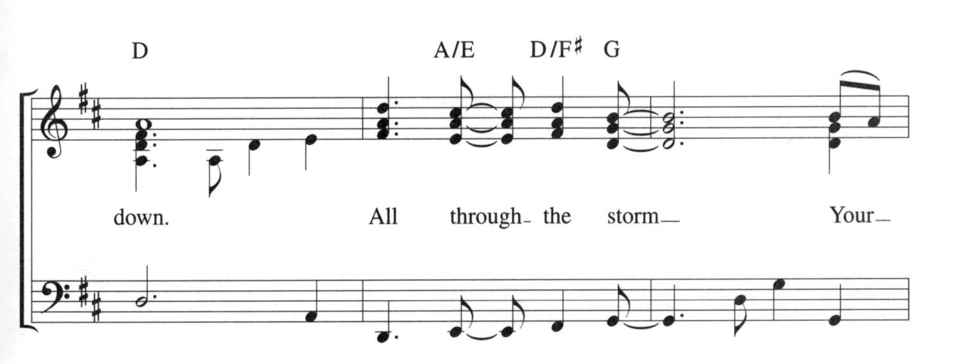
D
A/E
D/F♯
G
down. All through the storm Your

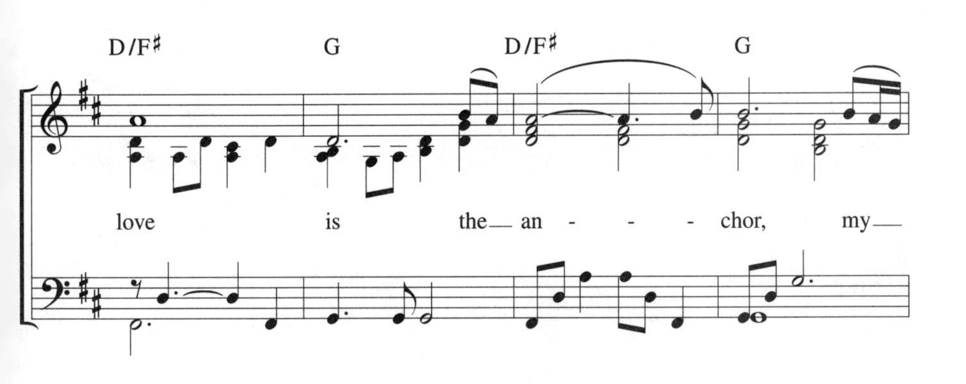
D/F♯
G
D/F♯
G
love is the an - - - chor, my

D/F♯
G
D/A
A
D
hope is in You a - lone.

Father God, I Wonder

(I Will Sing Your Praises)

Ian Smale

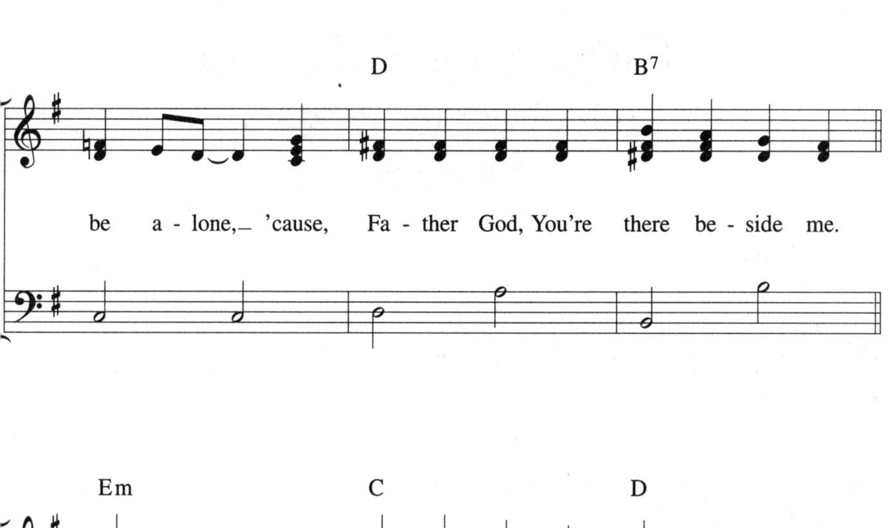
D
B7
be a - lone, 'cause, Fa - ther God, You're there be - side me.

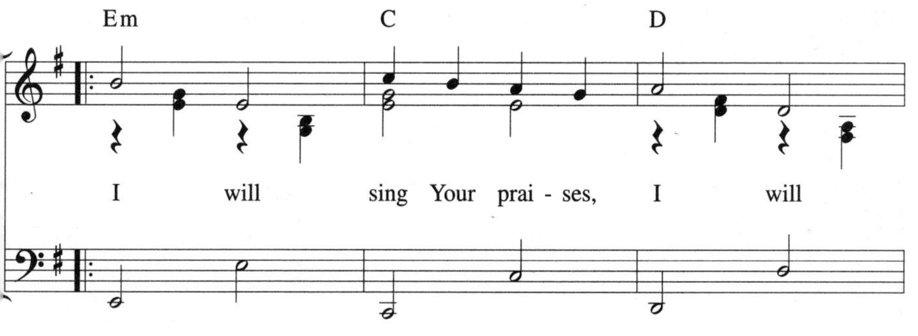
Em
C
D
I will sing Your prai - ses, I will

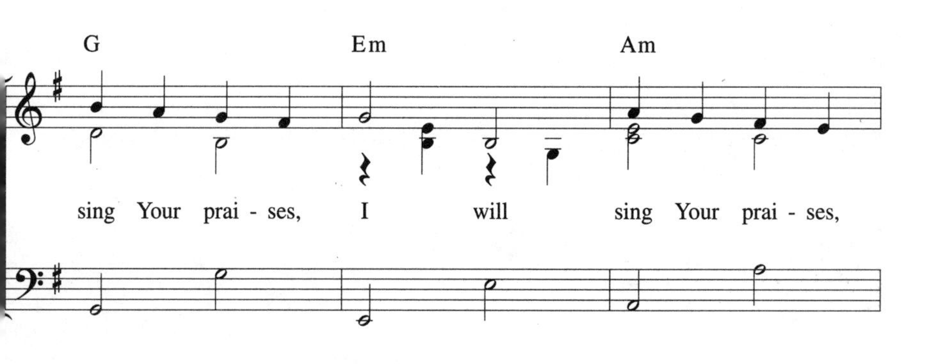
G
Em
Am
sing Your prai - ses, I will sing Your prai - ses,

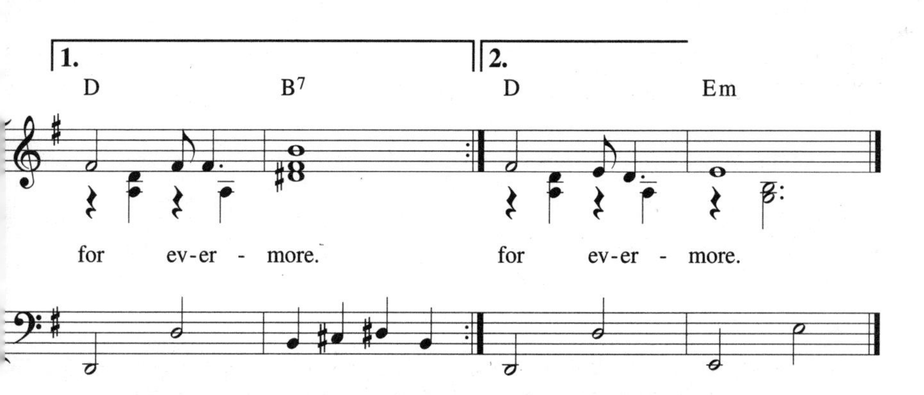
1.
2.
D
B7
D
Em
for ev-er - more.
for ev-er - more.

Father In Heaven, How We Love You

(Blessed Be The Lord God Almighty)

Bob Fitts

For I'm Building A People Of Power

Dave Richards

Father, I Place Into Your Hands

Jenny Hewer

Verse 2:
Father, I place into Your hands
My friends and family.
Father, I place into Your hands
The things that trouble me.
Father, I place into Your hands
The person I would be
For I know I always can trust You.

Verse 3:
Father, we love to see Your face
We love to hear Your voice
Father, we love to sing Your praise
And in Your name rejoice
Father, we love to walk with You
And in Your presence rest
For we know we always can trust You.

Verse 4:
Father, I want to be with You
And do the things You do.
Father, I want to speak the words
That You are speaking too.
Father, I want to love the ones
That You will draw to You
For I know that I am one with You.

For The Joys And For The Sorrows

(For This I Have Jesus)

Graham Kendrick

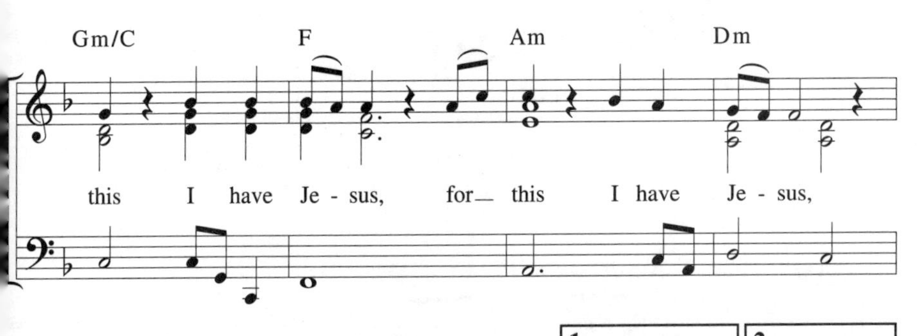

Verse 2:
For the tears that flow in secret
In the broken times
For the moments of elation
Or the troubled mind
For all the disappointments
Or the sting of old regrets
All my prayers and longings
That seem unanswered yet.

Verse 3:
For the weakness of my body
The burdens of each day
For the nights of doubt and worry
When sleep has fled away
Needing reassurance
And the will to start again
A steely-eyed endurance
The strength to fight and win.

For This Purpose

Graham Kendrick

Am Am7/G Am/F♯ Gsus4 G
Chorus
Men
glad-ness we sing and wel-come His king-dom in. Ov-er
Rhythmic
C F C F C F C D G D
Women
Men
Women
sin He has con-quer'd, hal-le-lu-jah, He has con-quer'd. Ov-er death vic-to-rious, hal-le-
G D G D E Am E
Men
Women
-lu-jah, vic-to-rious. Ov-er sick-ness He has tri-umph'd, hal-le-
Am E Am E F Gsus4 G7
All
-lu-jah, He has tri-umphed, Je-sus reigns ov-er
1. 2.
C F C Gsus4 C Gsus4 C
all!
Verse 2:
In the name of Jesus we stand
By the power of His blood
We now claim this ground.
Satan has no authority here
Pow'rs of darkness must flee
For Christ has the victory.

For Unto Us A Child Is Born

David Hadden

Verse 2:
And there shall be no end
To the increase of His rule
To the increase Of His government and peace
For He shall sit on David's throne
Upholding righteousness
Our God shall accomplish this.

Verse 3:
For He is the mighty God
He is the Prince of Peace
The King of Kings and Lord of Lords
All honour to the King
All glory to His name
For now and evermore.

From Heaven You Came, Helpless Babe

(The Servant King)

Graham Kendrick

Verse 2:
There in the garden of tears
My heavy load He chose to bear
His heart with sorrow was torn.
'Yet not my will but yours,' He said.

Verse 3:
Come see His hands and His feet
The scars that speak of sacrifice
Hands that flung stars into space
To cruel nails surrendered.

Verse 4:
So let us learn how to serve
And in our lives enthrone Him
Each other's needs to prefer
For it is Christ we're serving.

Give Thanks With A Grateful Heart

Henry Smith

2, 𝄋.
Gm7/C C C/B♭ Am Dm7 C/D Dm
Son. And now let the weak say, 'I am

Gm7 C B♭/D C/E
strong,' let the poor say, 'I am

Fmaj7 Am/E Dm7
rich,' be-cause of what the Lord has

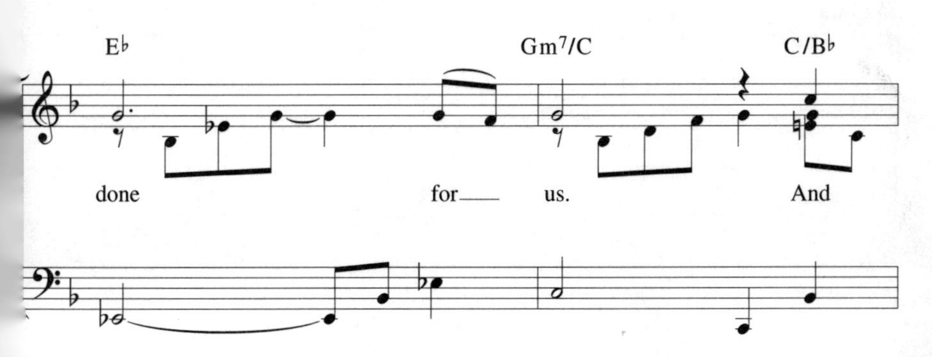
E♭ Gm7/C C/B♭
done for us. And

Am Dm7 C/D Dm Gm7
now let the weak say, 'I am strong,' let the

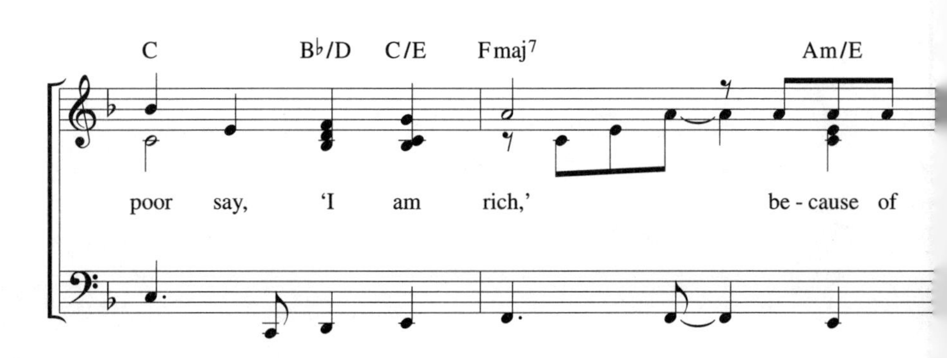
C B♭/D C/E Fmaj7 Am/E
poor say, 'I am rich,' be - cause of

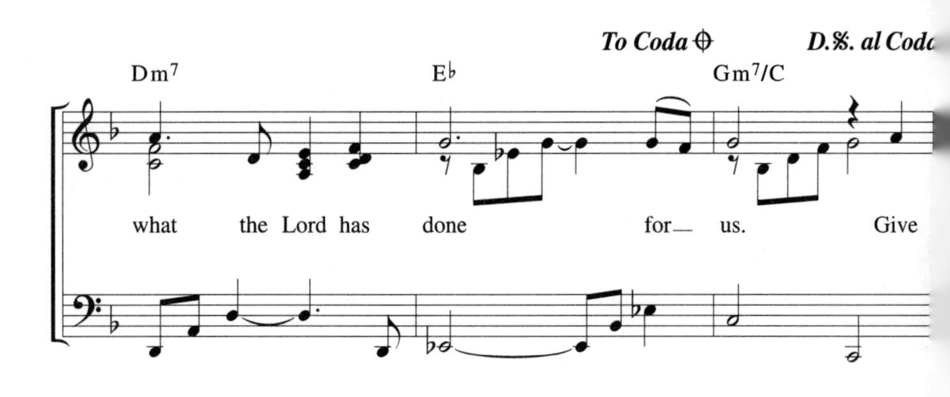
To Coda
D.S. al Coda
Dm7 E♭ Gm7/C
what the Lord has done for us. Give

Coda
Gm7/C C Csus4 F
us. Give thanks.

God Will Make A Way

Don Moen

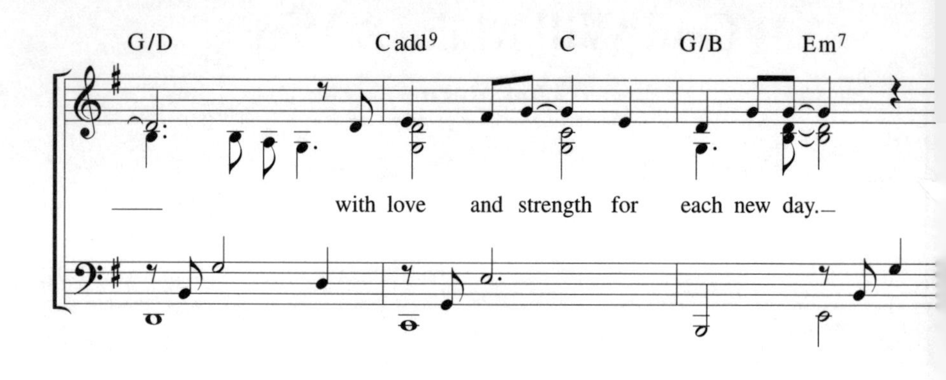
G/D Cadd9 C G/B Em7
with love and strength for each new day.

Am7 Bm7 Em7 Am7 C/D
He will make a way, He will make a

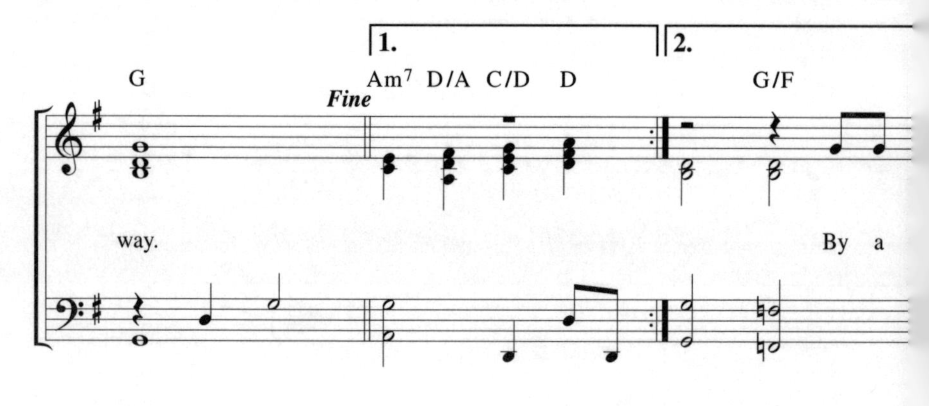
1. 2.
G Am7 D/A C/D D G/F
Fine
way. By a

E♭ F E♭/F E♭/B♭ B♭
road - way in the wil - der - ness He'll lead me,

A♭/B♭ B♭
E♭
F
and ri - vers in the des - ert will I

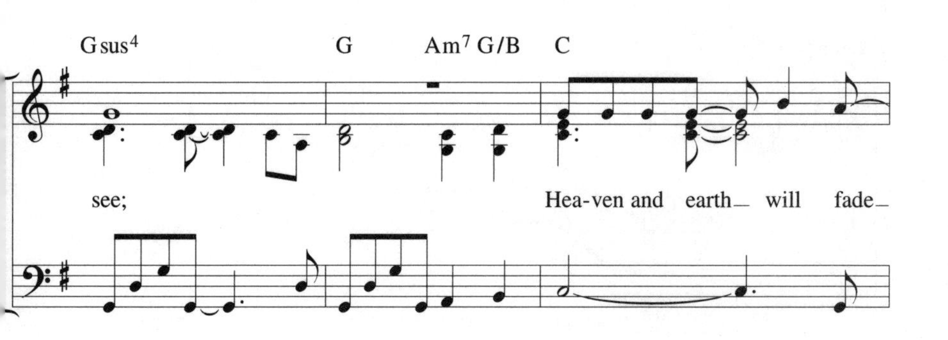
Gsus4
G
Am7 G/B
C
see;
Hea-ven and earth will fade

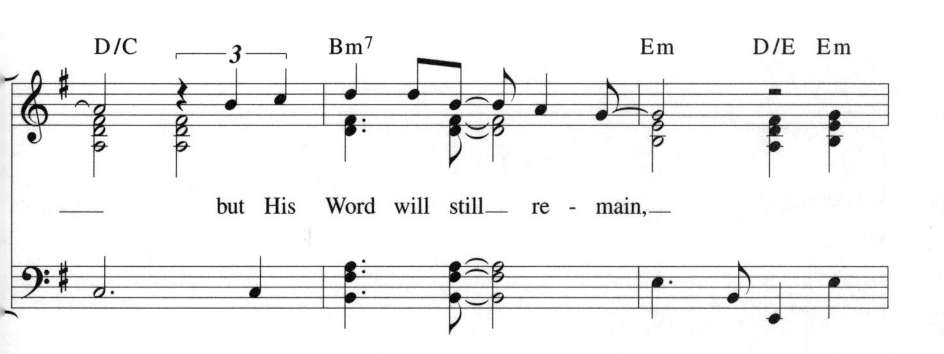
D/C
3
Bm7
Em
D/E
Em
but His Word will still re - main,

D.C. al Fine
Am7
Bm7
Esus4
E
C/D
D
He will do some-thing new to - day.

God Of Glory, We Exalt Your Name

David Fellingham

Descant
In pow'r res - plen - dent You reign in glo - ry,
Bm
F♯m
- plen - dent You reign in glo - ry, e - ter - nal
e - ter - nal King, You reign for ev - er.
Em
A
King, You reign for ev - er. Your word is
Your word is migh - ty, re-leas-ing cap - tives,
Bm
F♯m
migh - ty, re - leas - ing cap - tives, Your love is
Your love is gra-cious, You are my God.
Em
A7
D
G
D
gra - cious, You are my God.

God Of Grace

(I Stand Complete In You)

Chris Bowater

Am Em7 Dm7 G
on - ly grace pro - vides the way for me to stand com -
Csus4 C G/B Am Em7 Dm7
-plete. And Your grace clothes me in right - eous-
Gsus4 G Am Em7 F
-ness, and Your mer - cy cov-ers me in love.
G E7 Am Em7 F
Your life a - dorns and beau - ti - fies,
C Dm7 Gsus4 G C Csus4 C
I stand com-plete in You.

Great Is The Darkness

(Come, Lord Jesus)

Gerald Coates / Noel Richards

Verse 2:
May now your church rise with power and love
This glorious gospel proclaim.
In ev'ry nation salvation will come
To those who believe in your name.
Help us bring light to this world
That we might speed your return.

Verse 3:
Great celebrations on that final day
When out of the heavens you come.
Darkness will vanish, all sorrow will end
All rulers will bow at your throne.
Our great commission complete
Then face to face we shall meet.

Great Is The Lord

Steve McEwan

D/A
A
Lord, in whom we have the vic - to - ry.
He

D/A
F♯m
aids us a - gainst the e - ne - my,
we

A/E
Bm7
D/E E D/F♯ E
bow down on our knees.
And,

A
C♯m7
Lord, we want to lift your name on high,
and,

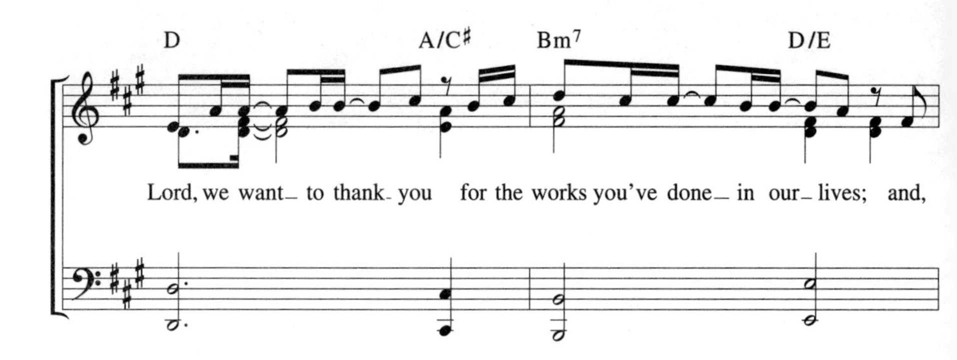
D
A/C♯
Bm7
D/E
Lord, we want to thank you for the works you've done in our lives; and,

A
C♯m7
Lord, we trust in your un - fail - ing love, for

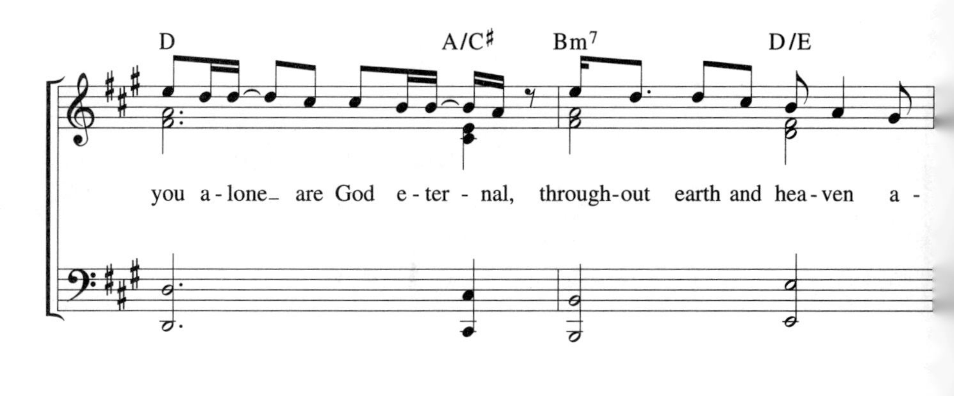
D
A/C♯
Bm7
D/E
you a - lone are God e - ter - nal, through-out earth and hea - ven a -

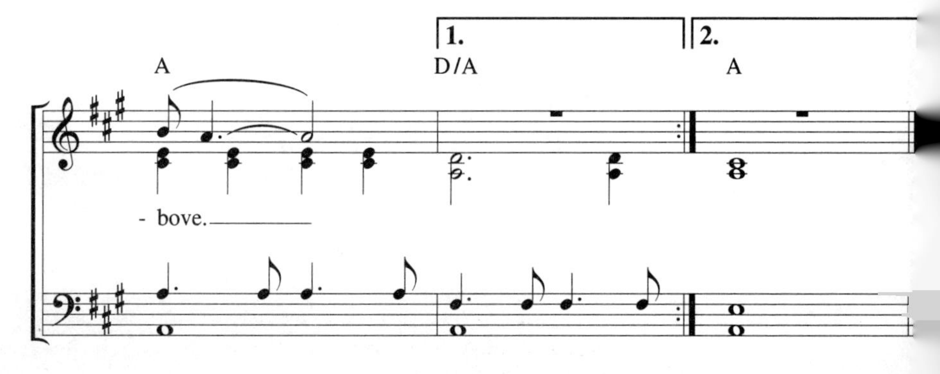
1.
2.
A
D/A
A
- bove.

He's Given Me A Garment Of Praise

David Hadden

G Em7 Am7 C/D To Coda
spi - rit of des - pair. He's giv - en me a
G G/B C D7
gar - ment of praise in - stead of a spi - rit of des -
1. G C D
- pair. He's giv-en me a
2. G
-pair.
B/D♯ Em D/F♯
A crown of beau - ty, in-stead of ash -
G G/B C
- es. The oil of glad - ness,

Am7
D
in-stead of mourn - ing.
My soul re - joic -
Em7
Em7/D
C
G/B
- es
as I de - light my - self in God.
Am7
Am7/D
He's giv - en me a gar - ment of praise in - stead
G
C
D
D.%. al Coda
of a spi - rit of des - pair.
He's giv-en me a
Coda
G
G/B
C
D7
G
gar-ment of praise in - stead of a spi - rit of des - pair.

Great Is Thy Faithfulness

Thomas O. Chisholm / William M. Runyan

Verse 2:
Summer and winter, and springtime and harvest
Sun, moon and stars in their courses above
Join with all nature in manifold witness
To thy great faithfulness, mercy and love.

Verse 3:
Pardon for sin and a peace that endureth
Thine own dear presence to cheer and to guide
Strength for today and bright hope for tomorrow
Blessings all mine, with ten thousand beside!

He Has Risen

Gerald Coates / Noel Richards / Tricia Richards

Verse 2:
In the grave God did not leave Him
For His body to decay
Raised to life, the great awakening
Satan's pow'r He overcame.

Verse 3:
If there were no resurrection
We ourselves could not be raised
But the Son of God is living
So our hope is not in vain.

Verse 4:
When the Lord rides out of heaven
Mighty angels at His side
They will sound the final trumpet
From the grave we shall arise.

Verse 5:
He has given life immortal
We shall see Him face to face
Through eternity we'll praise Him
Christ the champion of our faith.

He Is Exalted

Twila Paris

Am Em/G D/F♯ D G Bm7
He is the Lord, for - ev - er his truth shall
C G/B Am Em/G D/F♯ D
reign. Hea - ven and earth re -
2
2
G Bm7 C G/B Am Am/G
- joice in his ho - ly name. He is ex - alt - ed, the
Fmaj7 C/D G C/G G
King is ex - alt - ed on high.

He Is The Lord

(Show Your Power)

Kevin Prosch

D
G
He is the Lord. Who is like un - to him, nev-er
C
G
D
G
end - ing in days; he is the Lord. And
C
G
he comes in pow - er when we call on his name.
D
G
Chorus
He is the Lord. Show your
1.
G
Am7/G
G
D
pow - - - er, O Lord our God, show your

2.
D G Am7/G G
God, our God. 2. Your gos-pel, O Lord, is
C G D G
the hope for our na - tion; you are the Lord. It's the
C G D
pow-er of God for our sal-va-tion. You are the Lord.
G
We ask not for rich - es, but
C G D G
look to the cross; you are the Lord. And

C
G
for our in - he - ri - tance give us the lost.
D
G
Chorus
You are the Lord. Send your
G
Am7/G
G
pow - - - - er, O Lord our
1.
2.
D
D
G
Am7/G
God, send your God, our God.
G
D7sus4
C add9
Play 4 times

He Rescued Me

Geoff Baker

Verse 2:
The Father's arms are around me
The Spirit's fullness within
No condemnation now I fear
I rest secure in Him.

Verse 3:
To Jesus Christ be the glory
Almighty Saviour and friend
The love that bought me with His blood
Will keep me to the end.

Here I Am Wholly Available

Chris Bowater

Verse 2:
The time is right in the nation
For works of power and authority
God's looking for a people who are willing
To be counted in His glorious victory.

Verse 3:
As salt are we ready to savour?
In darkness are we ready to be light?
God's seeking out a very special people
To manifest His truth and His might.

Holiness Unto The Lord

Danny Daniels

Verse 2:
I love you, I love your ways
I love your name.
I love you, and all my days
I'll proclaim.

Holy Spirit, We Welcome You

Chris Bowater

Verse 2:
Holy Spirit, we welcome you
Holy Spirit, we welcome you
Let the breeze of Your presence blow
That Your children here might truly know
How to move the Spirit's flow.
Holy Spirit, Holy Spirit
Holy Spirit, we welcome you.

Verse 3:
Holy Spirit, we welcome you
Holy Spirit, we welcome you
Please accomplish in me today
Some new work of loving grace, I pray
Unreservedly have Your way.
Holy Spirit, Holy Spirit
Holy Spirit, we welcome you.

Hosanna

Carl Tuttle

Verse 2:
Glory, glory
Glory to the King of kings!
Glory, glory
Glory to the King of kings!
Lord, we lift up Your name
With hearts full of praise
Be exalted, O Lord, my God!
Glory to the King of kings!

How Can I Be Free From Sin

(Lead Me To The Cross)

Graham Kendrick / Steve Thompson

Verse 2:
How can I know peace within?
Lead me to the cross of Jesus
Sing a song of joy again
Lead me to the cross of Jesus.

Flowing from above
All-forgiving love
From the Father's heart to me.
What a gift of grace
His own righteousness
Clothing me in purity.

Verse 3:
How can I live day by day?
Lead me to the cross of Jesus
Following His narrow way
Lead me to the cross of Jesus.

How Deep The Father's Love For Us

Stuart Townend

Verse 2:
Behold the man upon a cross
My sin upon His shoulders
Ashamed, I hear my mocking voice
Call out among the scoffers.
It was my sin that held Him there
Until it was accomplished
His dying breath has brought me life
I know that it is finished.

Verse 3:
I will not boast in anything
No gifts, no pow'r, no wisdom
But I will boast in Jesus Christ
His death and resurrection.
Why should I gain from His reward?
I cannot give an answer
But this I know with all my heart
His wounds have paid my ransom.

How Good And How Pleasant

Graham Kendrick

Verse 2:
How deep are the rivers that run
When we are one in Jesus
And share with the Father and Son
The blessings of His everlasting life.

How Lovely On The Mountains

(Our God Reigns)

Leonard E. Smith Jnr

Verse 2:
You watchmen, lift your voices joyfully as one
Shout for your king, your king.
See eye to eye the Lord restoring Zion
Your God reigns, your God reigns!

Verse 3:
Waste places of Jerusalem, break forth with joy
We are redeemed, redeemed.
The Lord has saved and comforted his people
You God reigns, your God reigns.

Verse 4:
Ends of the earth, see the salvation of your God
Jesus is Lord, is Lord.
Before the nations he has bared his holy arm
Your God reigns, your God reigns.

I Am A New Creation

Dave Bilbrough

G A D G A D
You Lord, yes, I will praise You Lord, and I will sing
Bm G A
of all that You have done.
D A D
A joy that knows no li - mit, a light - ness in
G D G A
my spi - rit, here in the grace of God I stand.
1.
D G A
2.
D G D

I Believe In Angels

Stuart Bell / Johnny Markin / Paul Cruickshank

F♯m7 A/B E Esus4 E Asus2
1.
name of all.
2. B
Chorus
A E F♯m7 B
It's the high - est name, the name that's ov - er
Last time To Coda
1.
E A E D B E
all. It's the high - est name, the name on which we call. It's the
2.
E Esus4 E
Bridge
D A/C♯
call.
I be-lieve that suf - f'ring and
Am/C E/B D A/C♯
mar-tyrs cries will cease.
I be-lieve that heal - ing will

Verse 2:
I believe in worship that touches heaven's throne
I believe His Spirit renews the faithful one
I believe the Word of God, His truth revealed to all
Yes, I believe in Jesus, the highest name of all.

Verse 3:
I believe revival will touch the earth again
I believe His kingdomwill rule without an end
I believe that unity will see His blessing fall
For I believe in Jesus the highest name of all.

I Will Worship

(You Alone Are Worthy Of My Praise)

David Ruis

G
(I will seek you
I will seek you
F
)
all of my days.)
all of my days.
C
(I will fol - low
I will fol - low
G
)
Am7 D
(all your ways.
all of your ways.
G Chorus D/F♯
)
I will give you all my wor - ship,

Verse 2:
I will bow down (I will bow down,)
Hail you as King (hail you as King.)
I will serve you (I will serve you)
Give you ev'rything (give you ev'rything.)
I will lift up (I will lift up)
My eyes to your throne (my eyes to your throne.)
I will trust you (I will trust you)
I will trust you alone (trust in you alone.)

I Believe In Jesus

Marc Nelson

Verse 2:
I believe in you, Lord;
I believe you are the Son of God.
I believe you died and rose again
I believe you paid for us all.
(Men) And I believe you're here now
(Women) I believe that you're here
(All) Standing in our midst
(Men) Here with the power to heal now
(Women) With the power to heal
(All) And the grace to forgive.

I Believe The Promise

Russell Fragar

B♭ Dm7 Gm7 Cm7
there's a might - y sound and a torch of fire when we're
F Gm/F F B♭ D7(♭5) Gm7
ga-thered in one place. I be - lieve
Fm B♭7 E♭ B♭
that the pre - sence of God is here;
Dm7 Gm7 Cm7
there's not one thing that can't be changed when the Spi -
E♭ E♭/F
- rit of God is near.

B♭ D7(♭5) Gm7 Fm B♭7 E♭
I be - lieve that the pre - sence of God is here;
B♭ Cm7 Dm7 Gm7
when two or three are ga - thered, when
Cm7 Dm7 Gm7 F/G Cm7 Dm7
peo-ple rise in faith, I be-lieve God ans -
Last time
To Coda
Gm7 Cm7 E♭/F F7 A♭/B♭
1.
D.C.
- wers and His pre-sence is in this place.
2.
B♭ A♭/B♭
No - thing in earth or hea - ven can stop the

Bb
pow'r of God;
in - to our hand is gi - ven
Ab/Bb
A/B Bb/C
the call to take it on;
no o - cean
C Bb/C
A/B Bb/C
can con - tain it,
no star can rise a - bove;
C Bb/Eb
Eb/F
in - to our hearts is gi - ven
the pow'r of His love.
D.S. al Coda
F7
Coda
Cm7 Eb/F Bb
pre - sence is in this place

I Could Sing Unending Songs

(The Happy Song)

Martin Smith

1.
E
B/D♯
My heart is burst - ing, Lord, to tell of all You've done.
Aadd9
E/G♯
B
Of how You changed my life and wiped a - way the past.
E
B/D♯
I wan-na shout it out, from ev-'ry roof - top sing.
Aadd9
E/G♯
B
For now I know that God is for me, not a-gainst me.
2.
A
Ev-'ry-bo-dy's sing-ing now, 'cause we're so

E
hap - py!
A
Ev - 'ry - bo - dy's danc-ing now,
'cause we're so
E
hap - py.
If
F♯m7
A
on - ly we could see Your face
and see You smil-ing ov - er us
F♯m
A
un - seen an - gels ce - le-brate,
for joy is in this

E
B/D♯
place.
C♯m7
A7
E
B/D♯
C♯m7
A7
D.%. al Coda
O,
Coda
A
E
love.

I Give You All The Honour

(I Worship You)

Carl Tuttle

Verse 2:
As your Spirit moves upon me now
You meet my deepest need
And I lift my hands up to your throne
Your mercy I've received.

Verse 3:
You have broken chains that bound me
You've set this captive free
I will lift my voice to praise your name
For all eternity.

I Want To Be Out Of My Depth In Your Love

Doug Horley / Noel Richards

Verse 2:
Things I have held so tight
Made my security
Give me the strength I need
To simply let go.

I Want To Serve The Purpose Of God
(In My Generation)
Mark Altrogge

Verse 2:
I want to build with silver and gold in my generation
I want to build with silver and gold while I am alive.
I want to give my life *etc.*

Verse 3:
I want to see the kingdom of God in my generation
I want to see the kingdom of God while I am alive.
I want to give my life *etc.*

Verse 4:
I want to see the Lord come again in my generation
I want to see the Lord come again while I am alive.
I want to give my life *etc.*

I Was Made To Praise You

Chris Christensen

Verse 2:
I will always praise You
I will always glorify Your name
In every circumstance
I'll find a chance to thank You.
I will always love You
I will always worship at Your feet
And I'll obey You, Lord
I was made for You.

I Will Offer Up My Life

(This Thankful Heart)

Matt Redman

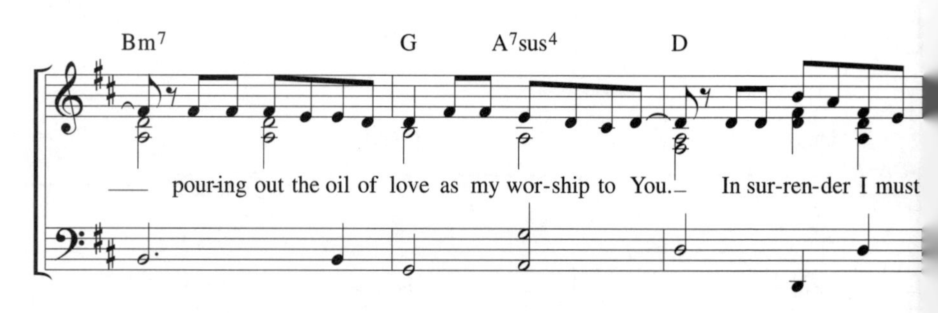

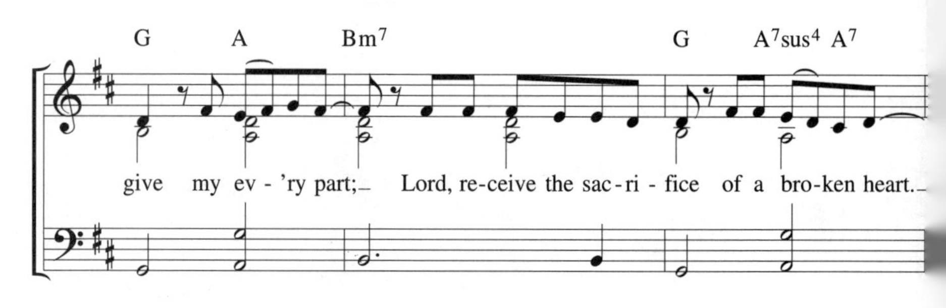

Verse 2:
You deserve my ev'ry breath
For you've paid the great cost
Giving up Your life to death
Even death on a cross
You took all my shame away
There defeated my sin
Opened up the gates of heav'n
And have beckoned me in.

I Worship You, Almighty God

Sondra Corbett

C/G G Em
give you praise, for you are my

Am7 D D7
right - eous - ness. I

Gsus4 G Em
wor - ship you, Al - migh - ty God,

Am7 C/D D7 G
there is none like you.

I'm Accepted, I'm Forgiven

Rob Hayward

Isn't He Beautiful

John Wimber

Verse 2:
Yes, You are beautiful,
Beautiful, yes You are…

I'm Special

Graham Kendrick

G
A
F♯7
B7
Thank You, Je - sus, thank You, Lord, for lov - ing me so

Em7
A7
D
D7
much. I know I don't de - serve an - y - thing;

G
A
F♯7
B7
help me feel Your love right now to know deep in my

Em7
A7
G
D
heart that I'm Your spe - cial friend.

I, The Lord Of Sea And Sky

(Here I Am, Lord)

Daniel L. Schutte

Verse 2:
I, the Lord of snow and rain
I have borne my people's pain
I have wept for love of them
They turn away.
I will break their hearts of stone
Give them hearts for love alone
I will speak my word to them
Whom shall I send?

Verse 3:
I, the Lord of wind and flame
I will tend the poor and lame
I will set a feast for them
My hand will save.
Finest bread I will provide
Till their hearts be satisfied
I will give my life to them
Whom shall I send?

In Heavenly Armour

(The Battle Belongs To The Lord)

Jamie Owens-Collins

Verse 2:
When the Power of Darkness comes in like a flood
The battle belongs to the Lord
He'll raise up a standard, the power of His blood
The battle belongs to the Lord.

Verse 3:
When your enemy presses in hard, do not fear
The battle belongs to the Lord
Take courage my friend, your redemption is near
The battle belongs to the Lord.

It's Your Blood

Michael Christ

Jesus Christ
(Once Again)
Matt Redman

Chorus
A♭ E♭ B♭ E♭ E♭sus4
I'm in that place once a - gain. And
E♭/G A♭ E♭/G B♭sus4 B♭
once a - gain I look up - on the cross where You died. I'm
E♭/G A♭ E♭/G B♭sus4 B♭
hum - bled by Your mer - cy and I'm bro - ken in - side.
Cm A♭ E♭/G B♭
Once a - gain I thank You, once a - gain I pour out my life.
1.
2.
Fine
A♭/C B♭sus4 B♭ E♭ E♭

Verse 2:
Now You are exalted to the highest place
King of the heavens, where one day I'll bow.
But for now I marvel at this saving grace
And I'm full of praise once again
I'm full of grace once again.

Jesus Is King

Wendy Churchill

Verse 2:
We have a hope that is steadfast and certain
Gone through the curtain and touching the throne
We have a Priest who is there interceding
Pouring his grace on our lives day by day.

Verse 3:
We come to Him, our Priest and Apostle
Clothed in His glory and bearing His name
Laying our lives with gladness before Him
Filled with His Spirit we worship the King.

Verse 4:
O holy one, our hearts do adore you
Thrilled with our goodness we give you our praise
Angels in light with worship surround Him
Jesus, our Saviour, for ever the same.

Jesus, Lover Of My Soul

(It's All About You)

Paul Oakley

D Asus4 A
all my days for
D G Bm G
no-one else in his-to-ry is like You, and
D A G
his-to-ry it-self be-longs to You.
D G Bm G
Al-pha and O-me-ga, You have loved me, and
D G Asus4 A
Chorus
I will share e-ter-ni-ty with You. It's all a-bout

Bm G D A
You, Je - sus, and all this is for
Bm G D
You, for Your glo - ry and Your fame;
A Bm G
it's not a - bout me, as if You
D G D A
should do things my way You a - lone are God and I sur-ren-
G D
- der to Your ways.

Jesus Is Lord!

David Mansell

Verse 2:
Jesus is Lord! Yet from His throne eternal
In flesh He came to die in pain
On Calv'ry's tree.
Jesus is Lord! From Him all life proceeding
Yet gave His life a ransom
Thus setting us free.

Verse 3:
Jesus is Lord! O'er sin the mighty conqueror
From death He rose, and all His foes
Shall own His name.
Jesus is Lord! God sent His Holy Spirit
To show by works of power
That Jesus is Lord.

Jesus Is The Name We Honour

(Jesus Is Our God)

Phil Lawson Johnston

Verse 2:
Jesus is the name we worship
Jesus is the name we trust.
He is the King above all other kings
Let all creation stand and sing
That Jesus is our God.

Verse 3:
Jesus is the Father's splendour
Jesus is the Father's joy.
He will return to reign in majesty
And ev'ry eye at last will see
That Jesus is our God.

Jesus Put This Song Into Our Hearts

Graham Kendrick

Verse 2:
Jesus taught us how to live in harmony
Jesus taught us how to live in harmony
Diff'rent faces, diff'rent races, He made us one
Jesus taught us how to live in harmony.

Verse 3:
Jesus taught us how to be a family
Jesus taught us how to be a family
Loving one another with the love that He gives
Jesus taught us how to be a family.

Verse 4:
Jesus turned our sorrow into dancing
Jesus turned our sorrow into dancing
Changed our tears of sadness into rivers of joy
Jesus turned our sorrow into a dance.

Jesus Shall Take The Highest Honour

Chris Bowater

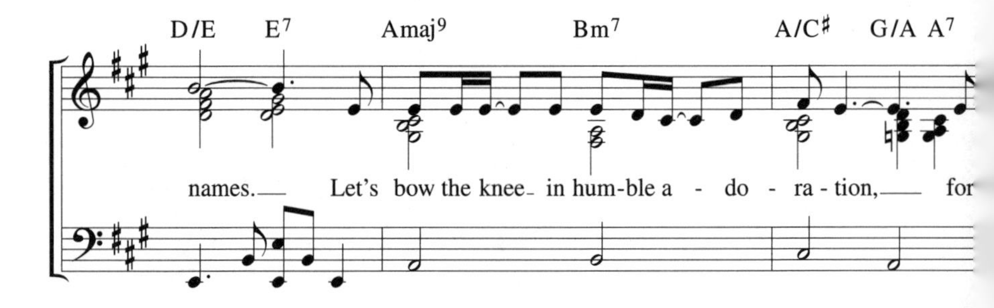

Dmaj7 E/D C#m7 F#m7 Bm7 E7
at His name ev-'ry knee must bow. Let ev-'ry tongue con-fess he is
Amaj7 F#m Dmaj7 B7/D#
Christ, God's on - ly Son, Sov-'reign Lord, we give you glo - ry
D/E E7 A C#m/G# F#m A/E
now. For all hon-our and bless-ing and pow-er
1. 2.
D A/C# Bm7 Esus4 E Bm7 Esus4 E
be-longs to You, be-longs to You. All be-longs to You, Lord
C#/E# F#m Bm7 D/E E6 A
Je-sus Christ, Son of the liv - ing God.

Jesus, Jesus
(Holy And Anointed One)
John Barnett

C add9
G add9
- ter to my soul. Your word is a lamp

C add9
Em7
un - to my feet. Je - sus, I love

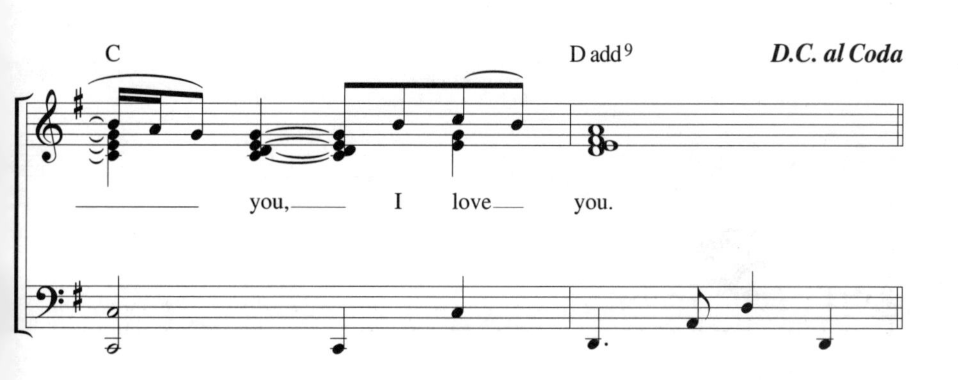
C
D add9
D.C. al Coda
you, I love you.

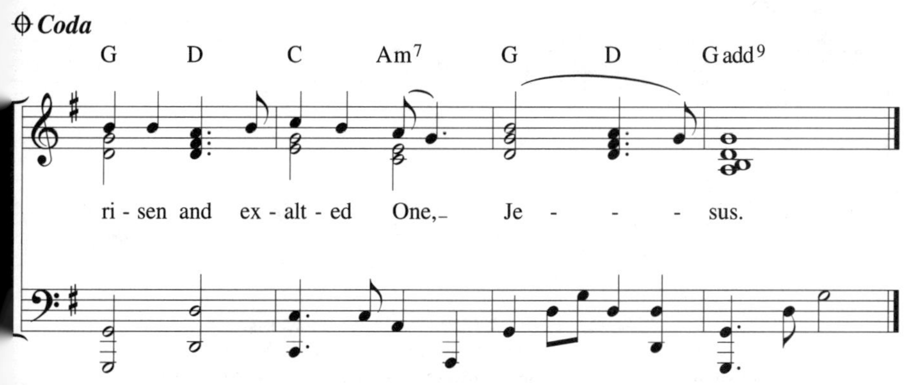
Coda
G D C Am7 G D G add9
ri - sen and ex - alt - ed One, Je - - - sus.

Jesus, We Celebrate Your Victory

John Gibson

G D Em D G D
Je - sus, we re - joice you've set
Last time To Coda
Em D G D Em D
us free; Je - sus, Your death has brought us
G C Verse
life. 1. It was for free-
D G D/F♯ Em
- dom that Christ has set us free, no
C D C
long - er to be sub - ject to a yoke of sla - ve - ry;

Verse 2:
His Spirit in us releases us from fear
The way to Him is open, with boldness we draw near.
And in His presence our problems disappear
Our hearts responding to His love.

Let There Be Love

Dave Bilbrough

Jesus, We Enthrone You

(Lord Jesus, We Enthrone You)

Paul Kyle

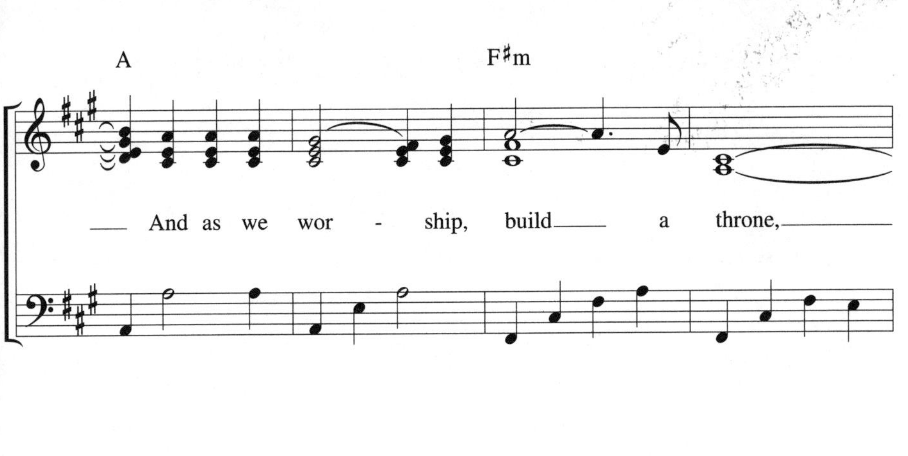
A F♯m
And as we wor - ship, build a throne,

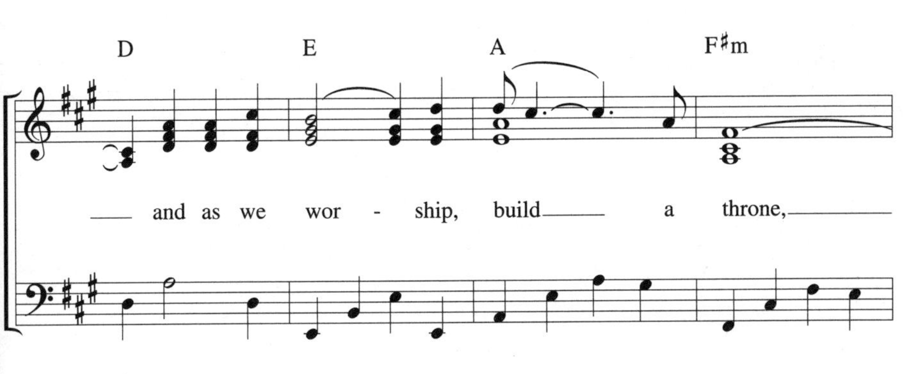
D E A F♯m
and as we wor - ship, build a throne,

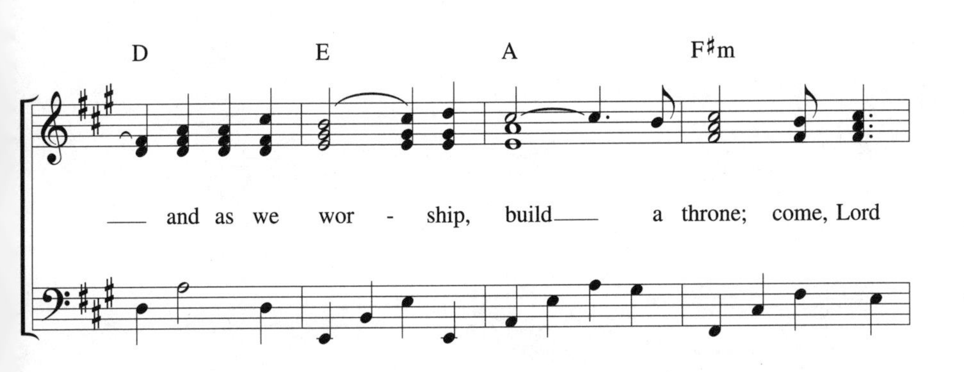
D E A F♯m
and as we wor - ship, build a throne; come, Lord

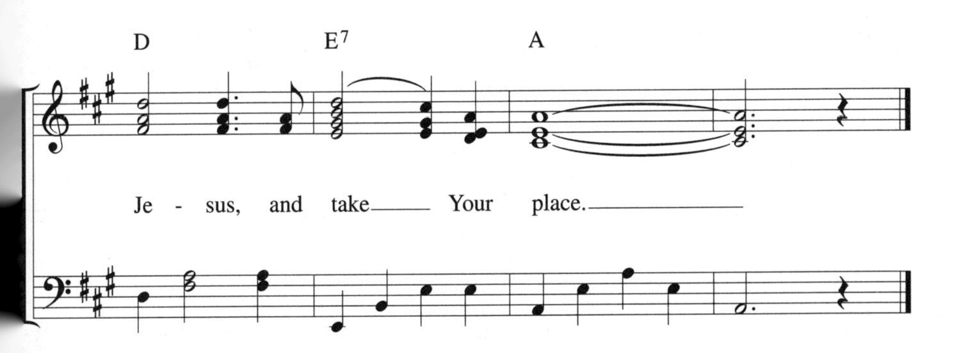
D E7 A
Je - sus, and take Your place.

Jesus, You Are Changing Me

Marilyn Baker

F
B♭7
seen in all I do.
Gm
Cm
Fm
B♭
You are the pot - ter and I am the clay,
G7
Cm
A♭
Fm7
B♭7
help me to be will - ing to let You have Your way.
E♭
B♭
E♭/C
B♭7/F E♭/G
Je - sus, You are chang - ing me, as I
A♭
E♭/B♭
B♭7
E♭
A♭m
E♭
let You reign su - preme with - in my heart.

King Of Kings, Majesty

Jarrod Cooper

Verse 2:
Earth and heav'n worship You
Love eternal, faithful and true
Who bought the nations, ransomed souls
Brought this sinner near to Your throne
All within me cries out in praise.

Lamb Of God

Chris Bowater

B7/D♯ A/E E D/E E D/A A
cleans - ing, still heal - - - ing. I ex - alt You,
A/G♯ F♯m Bm7
Je-sus my sac - ri - fice, I ex - alt You, my Re -
Bm/E Amaj9 D/E D/A A
- deem - er and my Lord. I ex - alt You,
A/G♯ F♯m Bm7
wor - thy Lamb of God, and in ho-nour I bow
E7 D 1. 2. A
down be-fore your throne.

Led Like A Lamb

(You're Alive)

Graham Kendrick

*Optional antiphonal alleluias: the congregation divides into three parts.

Verse 2:
At break of dawn, poor Mary
Still weeping she came
When through her grief she heard your voice
Now speaking her name.
(Men:) Mary, *(Women:)* Master,
(Men:) Mary, *(Women:)* Master.

Verse 3:
At the right hand of the Father
Now seated on high
You have begun Your eternal reign
Of justice and joy.
Glory, glory, glory, glory.

Let Your Living Water Flow

(Living Water)

John Watson

Verse 2:
Come now, Holy Spirit, and take control
Hold me in Your loving arms and make me whole
Wipe away all doubt and fear and take my pride
Draw me to Your love and keep me by Your side.

Verse 3:
Give your life to Jesus, let Him fill your soul
Let Him take you in His arms and make you whole
As you give your life to Him, He'll set you free
You will live and reign with Him eternally.

Verse 4:
Let Your living water flow over my soul
Let Your Holy Spirit come and take control
Of ev'ry situation that has troubled my mind
All my cares and burdens on to You I roll.

Lift Up Your Heads

Steven Fry

Verse 2:
Up from the dead He ascends
Through ev'ry rank of heav'nly power.
Let heaven prepare the highest place
Throw wide the everlasting doors.

Verse 3:
With trumpet blast and shouts of joy
All heaven greets the risen King
With angel choirs come line the way
Throw wide the gates and welcome Him.

Living Under The Shadow Of His Wing

David Hadden / Bob Silvester

Verse 2:
Bowed in adoration at His feet
We swell in harmony
Voices joined together that repeat
Worthy, worthy, worthy is the Lamb.

Verse 3:
Heart to heart embracing in His love
Reveals His purity
Soaring in my spirit like a dove
Holy, holy, holy is the Lord.

Lord I Come To You

(Power Of Your Love)

Geoff Bullock

F♯m
C♯m7
the weak-ness - es I see in me
F♯m
E
D
will be stripped a - way
E
Bm/E
D/A
A
E/G♯
F♯m
E
by the pow'r of Your love.
D
F♯m
E
Bm/A
Hold me close, let Your love sur - round
A
D
F♯m
E
me, bring me near, draw me to Your

Verse 2:
Lord, unveil my eyes
Let me see You face to face
The knowledge of Your love
As You live in me.
Lord, renew my mind
As Your will unfolds in my life
In living ev'ry day
In the pow'r of Your love.

Lord, For The Years

(Lord Of The Years)

Michael Baughen / Timothy Dudley-Smith

Verse 2:
Lord, for that word, the word of life which fires us
Speaks to our hearts and sets our souls ablaze
Teaches and trains, rebukes us and inspires us
Lord of the word, receive your people's praise.

Verse 3:
Lord, for our land, in this our generation
Spirits oppressed by pleasure, wealth and care
For young and old, for commonwealth and nation
Lord of our land, be pleased to hear our prayer.

Verse 4:
Lord, for our world; when we disown and doubt you
Loveless in strength, and comfortless in pain
Hungry and helpless, lost indeed without you
Lord of the world, we pray that Christ may reign.

Verse 5:
Lord, for ourselves; in living pow'r remake us
Self on the cross and Christ upon the throne
Past put behind us, for the future take us
Lord of our lives, to live for Christ alone.

Lord, I Lift Your Name On High

Rick Founds

G C D C
You came from hea - ven to earth to show the way,
G C D C
from the earth to the cross, my debt to pay,
G C D B7
from the cross to the grave, from the grave to the sky,
To Coda
Em Am7 D G C G D D.C. al Coda
Lord, I lift your name on high.
Coda
G C G D G
high.

Lord, The Light Of Your Love

(Shine, Jesus, Shine)

Graham Kendrick

Verse 2:
Lord, I come to Your awesome presence
From the shadows into Your radiance
By the blood I may enter Your brightness
Search me, try me, consume all my darkness.
Shine on me, shine on me.

Verse 3:
As we gaze on Your kingly brightness
So our faces display Your likeness
Ever changing from glory to glory
Mirrored here may our lives tell Your story.
Shine on me, shine on me.

(Chorus twice to end)

Lord, We Long For You

(Heal Our Nation)

Dave Bankhead / Ray Goudie / Patricia Morgan / Ian Townend

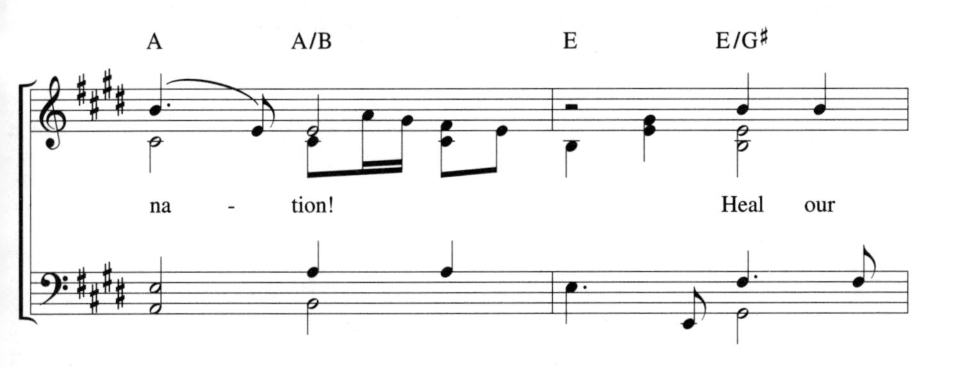

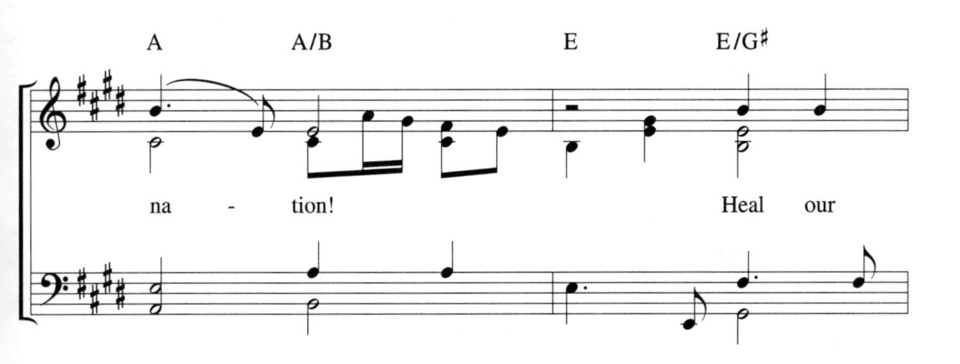

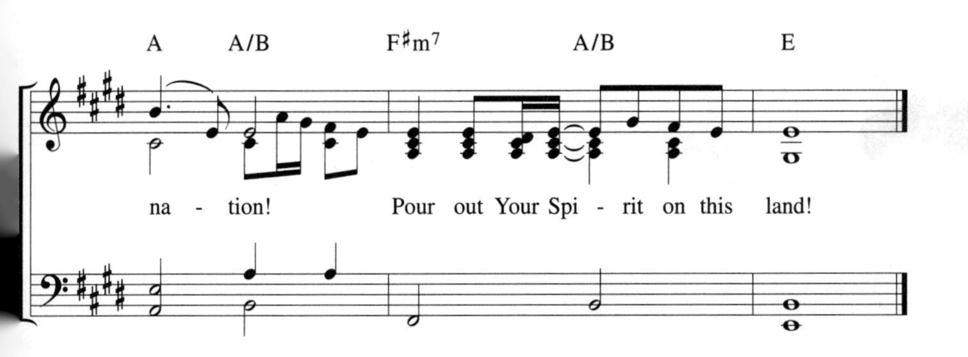

Verse 2:
Lord, we hear Your Spirit coming closer
A mighty wave to break upon our land
Bringing justice and forgiveness
God, we cry to You, 'Revive us!'

Lord, You Have My Heart

Martin Smith

(Women)
I will praise You, Lord.
D Dsus4 G D/F♯ Asus4 A D Dsus4
I will praise You, Lord. And I will
I will sing of love come down.
G D/F♯ Asus4 A D Dsus4
sing of love come down. And as You
Show Your face we'll see Your glo - ry
G D/F♯ Asus4 A G D/F♯ Asus4 A
show Your face, we'll see Your glo - ry
1.
2.
here.
D Dsus4 D Dsus4 D Dsus4 D
here.

Majesty

Jack Hayford

Am D G C/G G D
own, His an-them raise. So ex - alt, lift up on
Am C/D D G D
high the name of Je - sus; mag - ni - fy, come glo - ri -
Am D B D
- fy Christ Je - sus the King.
G C Am7 D7
Ma - jes - ty, wor-ship His ma - jes - ty, Je - sus who
G Em7 Am D G C/G G
died, now glo - ri - fied, King of all kings.

Make Me A Channel Of Your Peace

(Prayer Of St. Francis)

Sebastian Temple

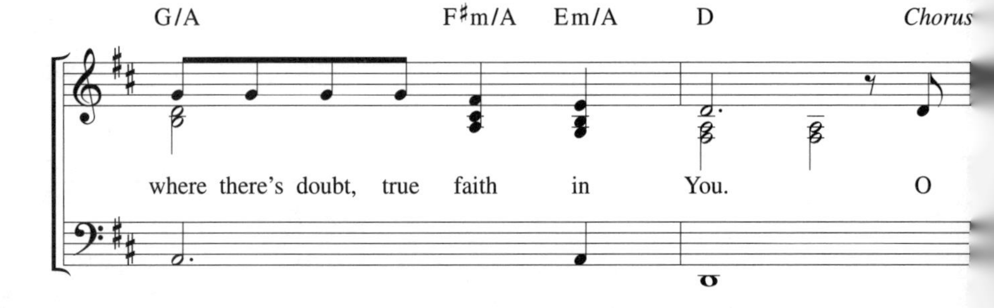

Verse 2:
Make me a channel of Your peace
Where there's despair in life, let me bring hope
Where there is darkness, only light
And where there's sadness, ever joy.

Verse 3:
Make me a channel of Your peace
It is in pardoning that we are pardoned
In giving of ourselves that we receive
And in dying that we're born to eternal life.

Make Way, Make Way

Graham Kendrick

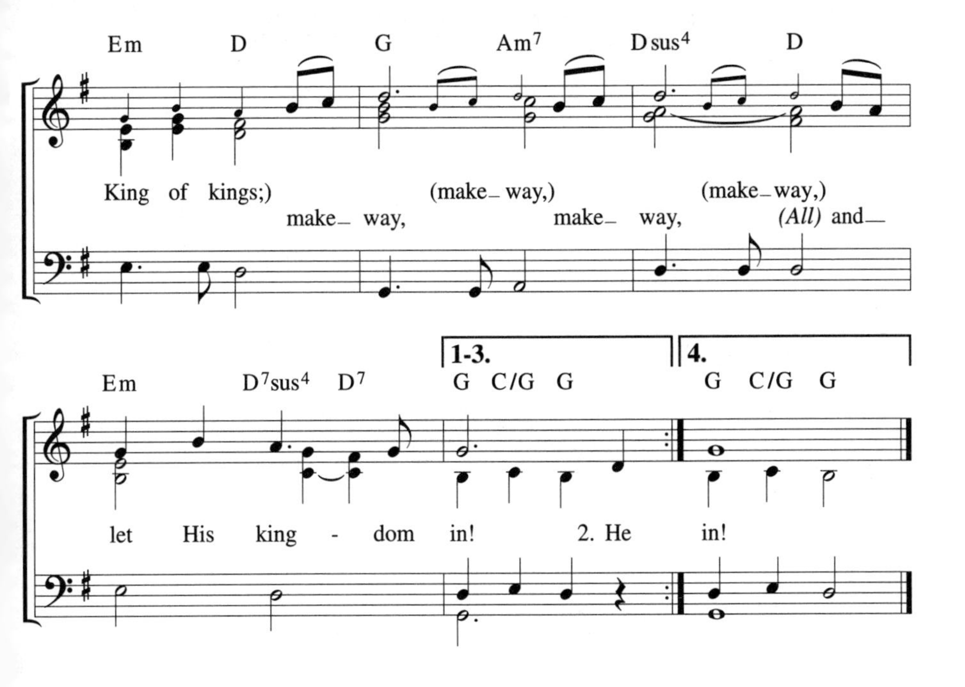

Verse 2:
He comes the broken hearts to heal
The pris'ners to free
The deaf shall hear, the lame shall dance
The blind shall see.

Verse 3:
And those who mourn with heavy hearts
Who weep and sigh
With laughter, joy and royal crown
He'll beautify.

Verse 4:
We call you now to worship Him
As Lord of all
To have no gods before Him
Their thrones must fall.

May The Fragrance

Graham Kendrick

Verse 2:

(Men)	May the glory of Jesus fill His church.
(Women)	May the glory of Jesus fill His church.
(Men)	May the glory of Jesus fill His church.
(Women)	Radiant glory of Jesus
(All)	Shining from our faces
	As we gaze in adoration.

Verse 3:

(Men)	May the beauty of Jesus fill my life.
(Women)	May the beauty of Jesus fill my life.
(Men)	May the beauty of Jesus fill my life.
(Women)	Perfect beauty of Jesus
(All)	Fill my thoughts, my words, my deeds
	May I give in adoration.
	Fill my thoughts, my words, my deeds
	May I give in adoration.

Meekness And Majesty

(This Is Your God)

Graham Kendrick

Verse 2:
Father's pure radiance
Perfect in innocence
Yet learns obedience
To death on a cross.
Suffering to give us life
Conquering through sacrifice
And as they crucify
Prays: 'Father forgive.'

Verse 3:
Wisdom unsearchable
God the invisible
Love indestructible
In frailty appears.
Lord of infinity
Stooping so tenderly
Lifts our humanity
To the heights of his throne.

Men Of Faith

(Shout To The North)

Martin Smith

C
Dsus4
G
C/E
D/F♯
east and the west.
Je - sus is Sa-viour to all,
Last time To Coda
1, 3.
C
D
Gsus2
G
Lord of hea-ven and earth.
2. Rise up,
2.
G
Em
C
We've been through fire, we've been through rain,
Em
C
D
we've been re - fined by the pow'r of His name.
Em
C
We've fall-en deep-er in love with You, You've burned the truth on our

Verse 2:
Rise up, women of the truth
Stand and sing to broken hearts.
Who can know the healing pow'r
Of our awesome King of love?

Verse 2:
Rise up, church with broken wings
Fill this place with songs again
Of our God who reigns on high
By His grace again we'll fly.

No Longer Mine, Lord

Geoff Baker

Verse 2:
No longer mine Lord, but Yours
To do with me as You desire
To be exalted, or laid aside
Take vain ambition and selfish pride
Let me be humbled, You glorified
No longer mine, no longer mine but Yours.

Verse 3:
No longer mine Lord, but Yours
The sovereign Lord who we adore
We bow before You our glorious King
Our very lives, Lord, we freely bring
A cov'nant human and divine
No longer mine, no longer mine but Yours.

Mighty God

Chris Bowater / Mark Johnson / Helen Johnson

Verse 2:
A light to those in darkness and a guide to paths of peace
Love and mercy dawns, grace, forgiveness and salvation
Light for revelation, glory to Your people
Son of the Most High, God's love-gift to all.

More Love, More Power

Jude del Hierro

Gm
Cm
and I will wor-ship you / seek your face with all of my strength,

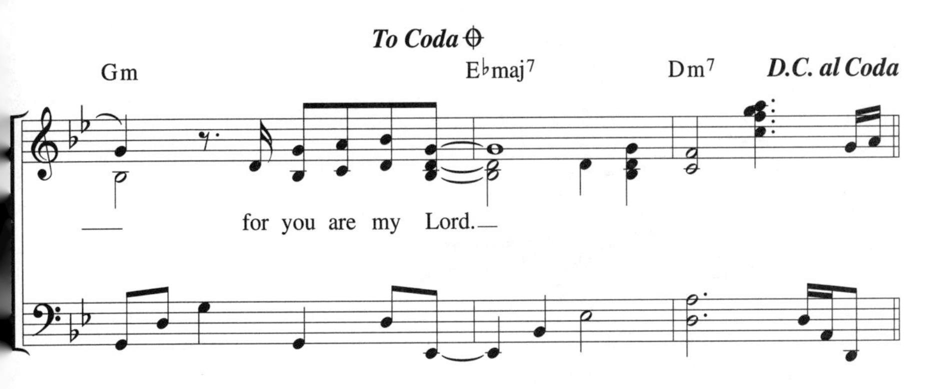
To Coda
Gm
E♭maj7
Dm7
D.C. al Coda
for you are my Lord.

Coda
E♭maj7
Dm
Gm
E♭maj7
For you are my Lord;

Dm7
Gm
you are my Lord.

My Jesus, My Saviour

(Shout To The Lord)

Darlene Zschech

A♭ Cm/G Fsus4 F B♭ Gm
wor - ship You.
Shout to the Lord, all the earth,
I sing for joy at the work
E♭ Fsus4 F B♭ Gm
let us sing pow - er and ma - jes - ty, praise
of Your hands. For ev - er I'll love You, for ev -
E♭ Fsus4 F Gm
to the King. Moun-tains bow down and the seas
- er I'll stand. No - thing com - pares to the pro -
1.
E♭ F Gm F/A
will roar at the sound of Your name.
2.
E♭ F B♭ B♭sus4 B♭
- mise I have in You.

My Lips Shall Praise You

(Restorer Of My Soul)

Noel Richards / Tricia Richards

Verse 2:
Love that conquers ev'ry fear
In the midst of trouble You draw near
You are the restorer of my soul.

Verse 3:
You're the source of happiness
Bringing peace when I am in distress
You are the restorer of my soul.

My Lord, What Love Is This?

(Amazing Love)

Graham Kendrick

Verse 2:
And so they watched Him die
Despised, rejected
But O, the blood He shed
Flowed for me!

Verse 3:
And now this love of Christ
Shall flow like rivers
Come, wash your guilt away
Live again!

O God Of Burning, Cleansing Flame

(Send The Fire)

William Booth (1829-1912) / Lex Loizides

Verse 2:
God of Elijah, hear our cry: send the fire!
And make us fit to live or die: send the fire today!
To burn up ev'ry trace of sin
To bring the light and glory in
The revolution now begin!
Send the fire today! Send the fire today!

Verse 3:
It's fire we want, for fire we plead: send the fire!
The fire will meet our ev'ry need: send the fire today!
For strength to always do what's right
For grace to conquer in the fight
For pow'r to walk the world in white.
Send the fire today! Send the fire today!

Verse 4:
To make our weak heart strong and brave: send the fire!
To live, a dying world to save: send the fire today!
O, see us on Your altar lay
We give our lives to You today
So crown the off'ring now we pray
Send the fire today! Send the fire today! Send the fire today!

O Lord Our God

(We Will Magnify)

Phil Lawson Johnston

Verse 2:
O Lord our God, You have established a throne
You reign in righteousness and splendour.
O Lord our God, the skies are ringing with Your praise
Soon those on earth will come to worship.

Verse 3:
O Lord our God, the world was made at Your command
In You all things now hold together.
Now to Him who sits on the throne and to the Lamb
Be praise and glory and pow'r for ever.

O Lord, My God

(How Great Thou Art)

Stuart K. Hine (1899-1989)

Verse 2:
When through the woods and forest glades I wander
And hear the birds sing sweetly in the trees
When I look down from lofty mountain grandeur
And hear the brook, and feel the gentle breeze.

Verse 3:
And when I think that God, His Son not sparing
Sent Him to die, I scarce can take it in
That on the cross, my burden gladly bearing
He bled and died to take away my sin.

Verse 4:
When Christ shall come with shout of acclamation
And take me home, what joy shall fill my heart
Then I shall bow in humble adoration
And there proclaim: my God, how great Thou art.

O Lord, Your Tenderness

Graham Kendrick

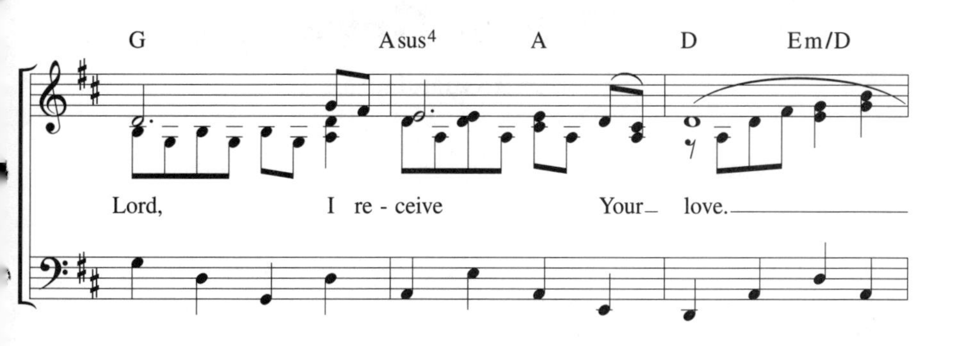
G Asus4 A D Em/D
Lord, I re - ceive Your love.

D7 G Asus4 A
O Lord, I re - ceive Your

D D7 G
love, O Lord, I re -

Asus4 A D G D
- ceive Your love.

Only By Grace

Gerrit Gustafson

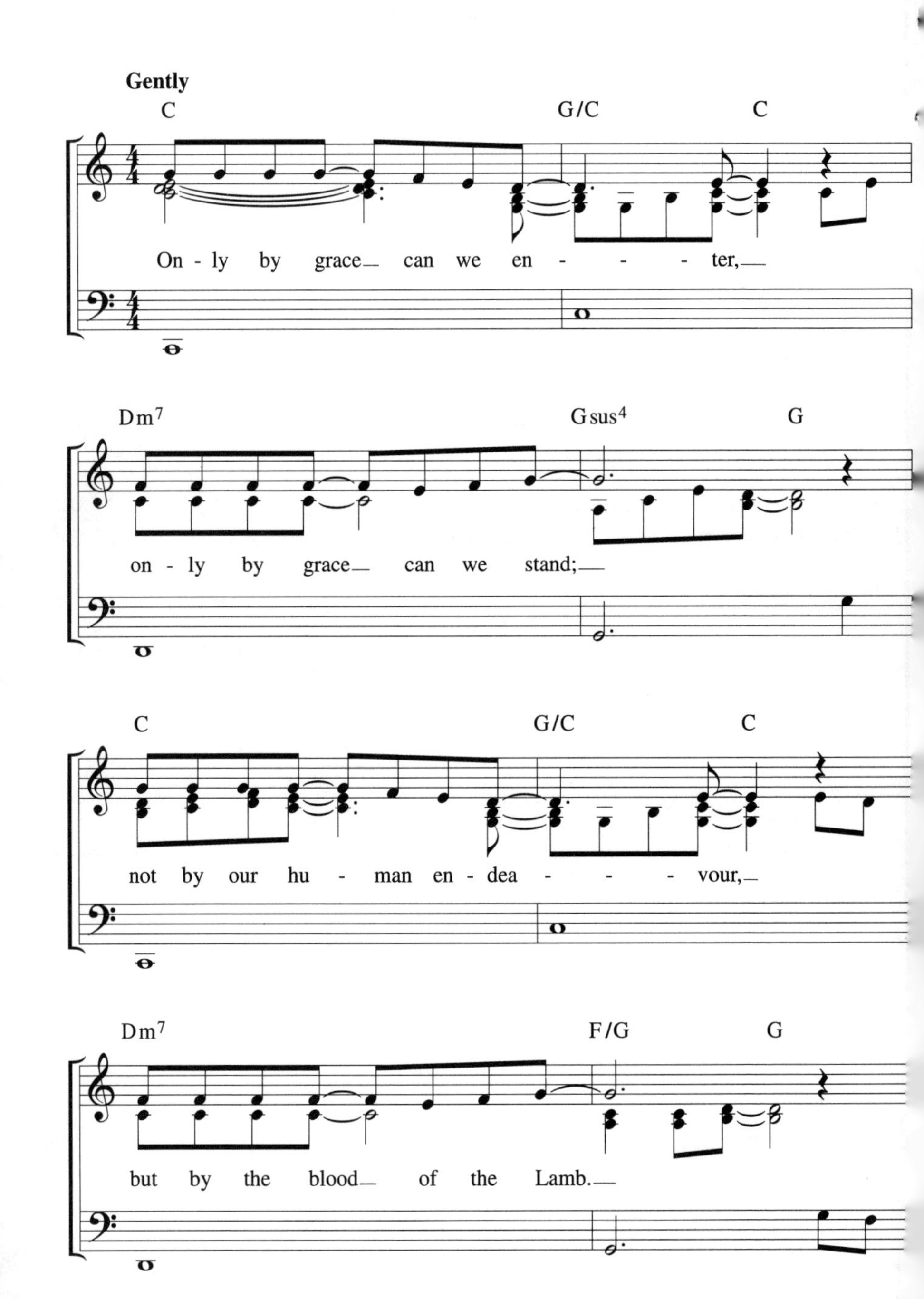

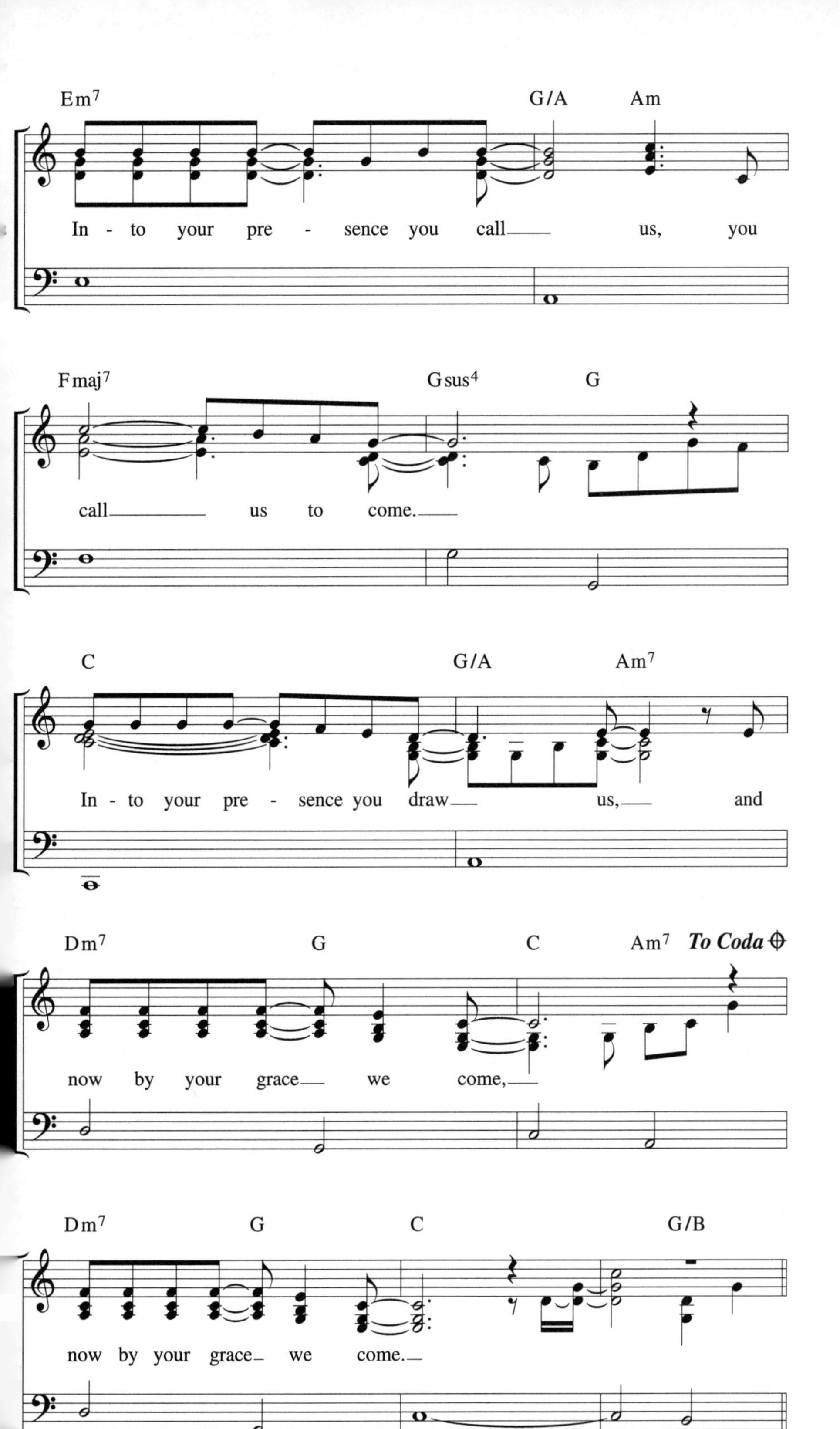
Em7
G/A
Am
In - to your pre - sence you call us, you
Fmaj7
Gsus4
G
call us to come.
C
G/A
Am7
In - to your pre - sence you draw us, and
Dm7
G
C
Am7
To Coda
now by your grace we come,
Dm7
G
C
G/B
now by your grace we come.

Am
G
F
F/G
G
Lord, if you mark our trans - gres - sions, who would
G/C
C
Dm/B
E7
stand?
Am
G
F
G
Thanks to your grace we are cleansed by the blood of the Lamb.
1.
2.
D.C. al Coda
Am
Dm7
E7
F/G
Gsus4
G
Coda
Dm7
G
C
now by your grace we come.

Open Your Eyes

Carl Tuttle

Open Our Eyes, Lord

Robert Cull

G
A7
Op - en our ears, Lord, and

G
D
Bm
help us to lis - - - ten.

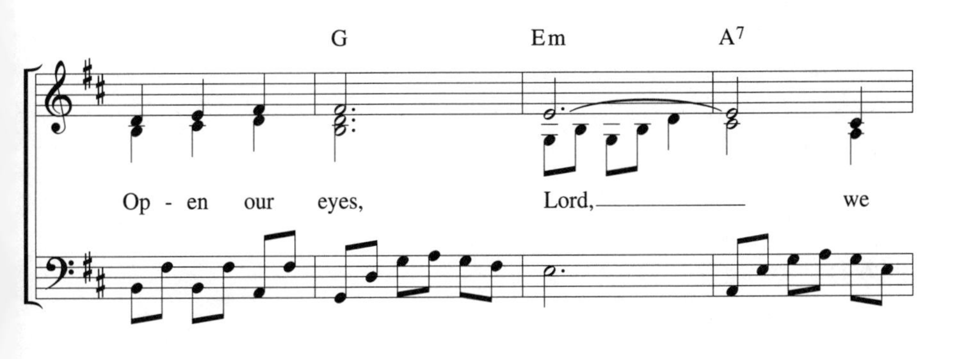
G
Em
A7
Op - en our eyes, Lord, we

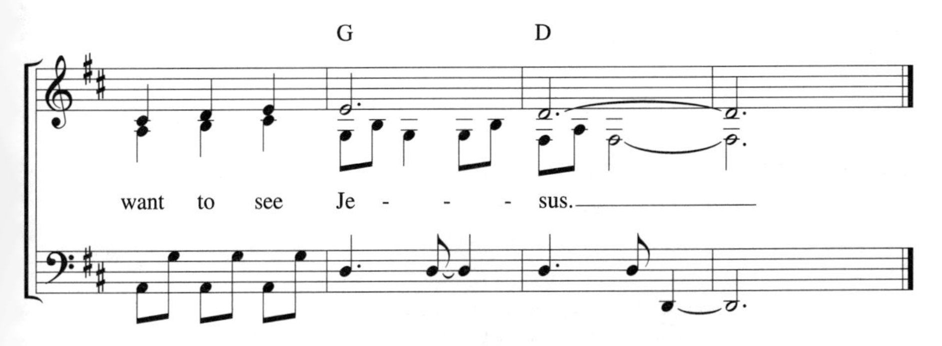
G
D
want to see Je - - - sus.

Our God Is An Awesome God

Rich Mullins

Praise God From Whom All Blessings Flow

Jimmy Owens

Over The Mountains And The Sea

(I Could Sing Of Your Love Forever)

Martin Smith

Csus4
F
Gm7
for ev - er,
I could sing of Your love
for ev - er,
To Coda
1.
2.
B♭
Csus4
Gm7
I could sing of Your love
for ev - er.
O, I feel like
F/A
B♭
Csus4
C
danc-ing,
it's fool-ish-ness, I
know;
Gm7
F/A
B♭
but when the world has seen the light, they will dance with joy like we're danc-
D.%. al Coda
Coda
Csus4
Csus4
F
- ing now.
for ev - er.

Praise God From Whom All Blessings Flow

Andrew Piercy / David Clifton

D
A/D
G
Bm
Bm/A
glo - ry to the Son,
give glo - ry to the Spi - rit while
G
A
D/A
A
D/A
end-less ag - es run.
'Wor - thy the Lamb,' all hea -
A
D
G
- ven cries, 'to be ex-alt-ed thus.'
'Wor-thy the Lamb,' our hearts
Bm
G
C
Asus4
A
re - ply, 'for He was slain for us.'
Praise
D
G
D
Bm
A
God from whom all bless - ings flow, praise Him all crea - tures here

G D G D
be - low. Praise Him a - bove, you heav'n - ly host, praise
Last time To Coda
1.
2.
Bm A G D G D
Fa-ther, Son and Ho - ly Ghost. Praise - ly Ghost. Praise
A/D D/A D A/D
God from whom all bless - ings flow, praise God from whom all bless-
1.
2. D.%. al Coda
Coda
A D A D G D
- ings flow. Praise ings flow. Praise - ly Ghost. Praise
Bm A G D Bm A G D
Fa-ther, Son and Ho - ly Ghost. Praise Fa-ther, Son and Ho - ly Ghost.

Reign In Me

Chris Bowater

Purify My Heart

(Refiner's Fire)

Brian Doerksen

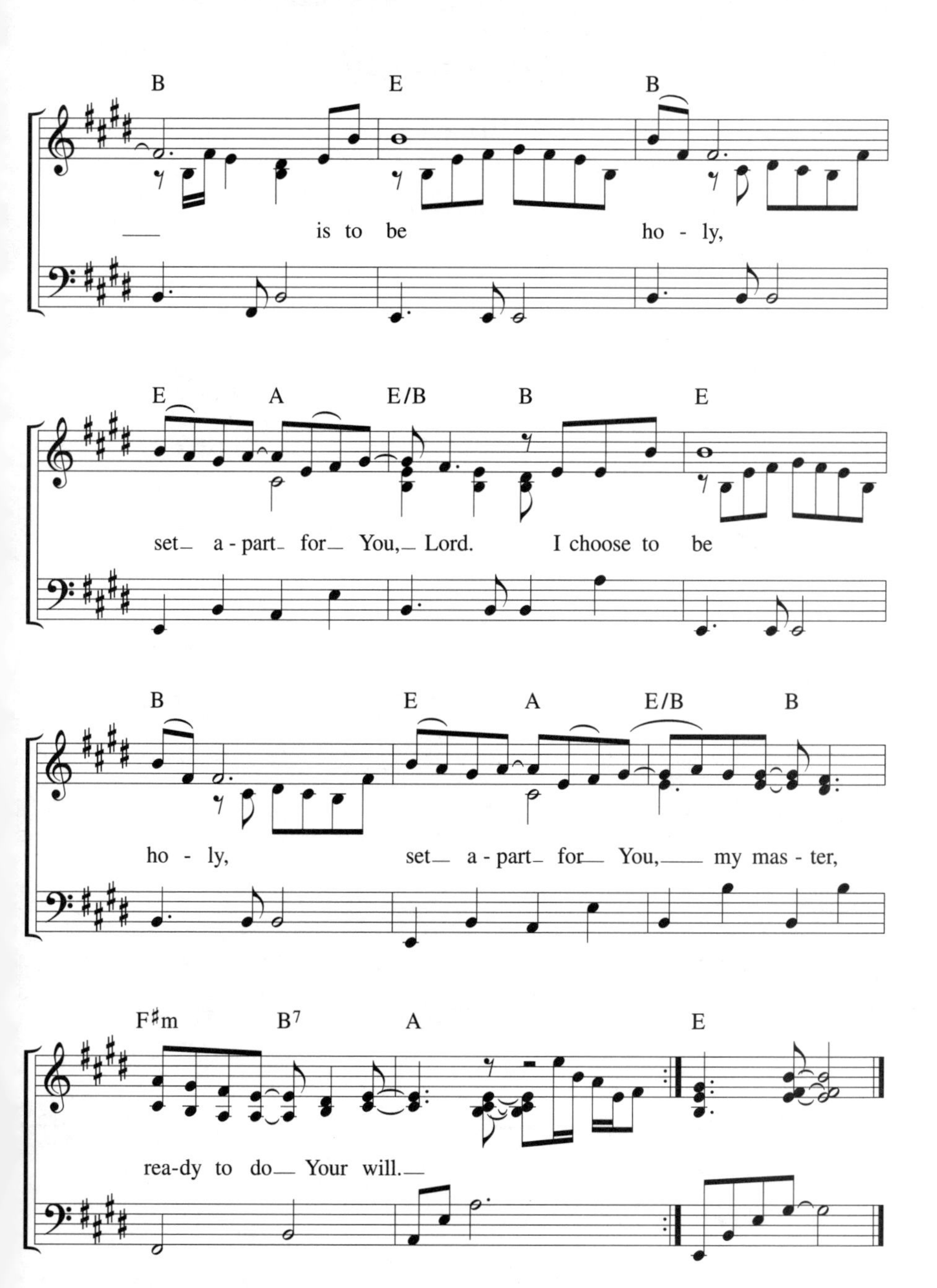

Verse 2:
Purify my heart
Cleanse me from within and make me holy.
Purify my heart
Cleanse me from my sin, deep within.

Reconciled

Mike Kerry

Verse 2:
Justified, I'm justified
It's just as if I'd never sinned
And once I knew such guilty fear
But now I know His peace within me.
Justified, I'm justified
It's all because my Jesus died.
I'm justified, I'm justified by God.

Hallelujah I'll…

Verse 3:
Magnify, I'll magnify
I'll magnify His name for ever
Wear the robe of righteousness
And bless the name of Jesus, Saviour
Magnify the One who died
The One who reigns for me on high.
I'll magnify, I'll magnify my God.

Rejoice!

Graham Kendrick

G/D
D
D
A/D
G/D
D
Verse
A
Bm
1. Now is the time for us to march up - on the land,
G
A
in - to our hands He will give the ground we
D
A
claim.
He rides in
Bm
ma - je - sty to lead us in - to vic - to - ry,

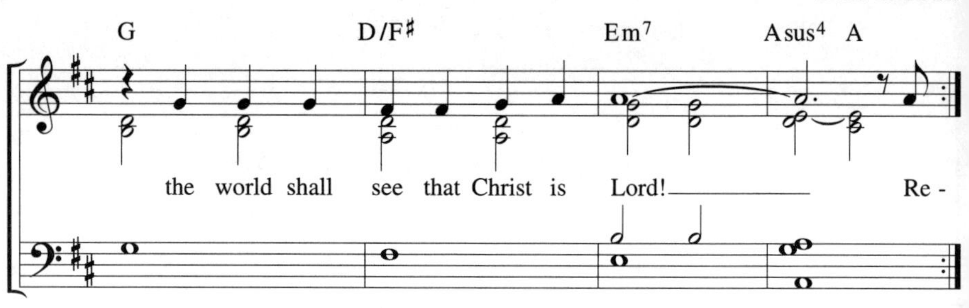

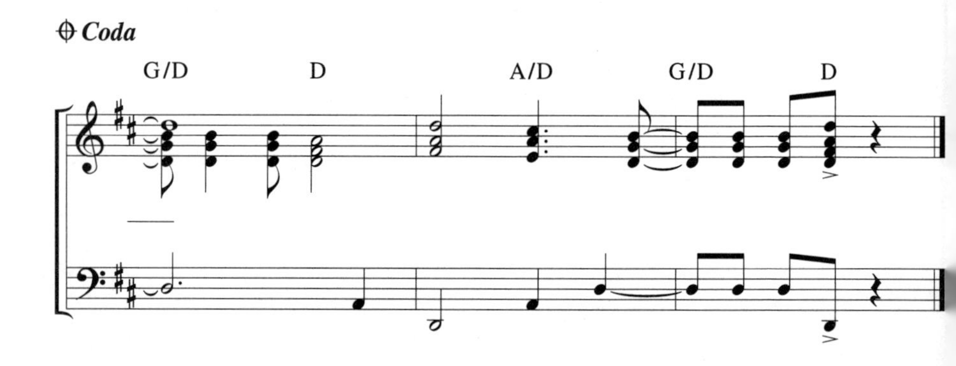

Verse 2:
God is at work in us
His purpose to perform
Building a kingdom
Of power not of words
Where things impossible
By faith shall be made possible
Let's give the glory to Him now.

Verse 3:
Though we are weak, His grace
Is ev'rything we need
We're made of clay
But this treasure is within.
He turns our weaknesses
Into His opportunities
So that the glory goes to Him.

Say The Word

Stuart Townend

2, 3.
E♭ B♭sus4 A♭/C B♭sus4 B♭7
His tears have fall - en like rain
E♭/G A♭ Fm7 A♭/E♭
on my life, each drop a fresh re - ve - la -
D♭maj7 E♭/G A♭/C B♭sus4 B♭7
- tion. I will re - turn to the place
E♭/G A♭ Fm7 Gm7 A♭ B♭
of the cross, where grace and mer - cy
D.%. al Cod
To Coda
Cm B♭/D C/E Fm Fm/E♭ B♭/D B♭sus4
pour from hea - ven's throne. 3. Say th

Verse 2:
Say the word, I will be filled
My hands reach out to heaven
Where striving is stilled.
Say the word, I will be changed
Where I am dry and thirsty
Send cool, refreshing rain
Say the word.

Verse 3:
Say the word, I will be poor
That I might know the riches
That you have in store.
Say the word, I will be weak
Your strength will be the power
That satisfies the meek
Say the word.

The Lord will see the travail of His soul
And He and I will be satisfied.
Complete the work You have started in me
O come, Lord Jesus, shake my life again.

Restore, O Lord

Graham Kendrick / Chris Rolinson

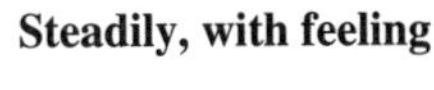

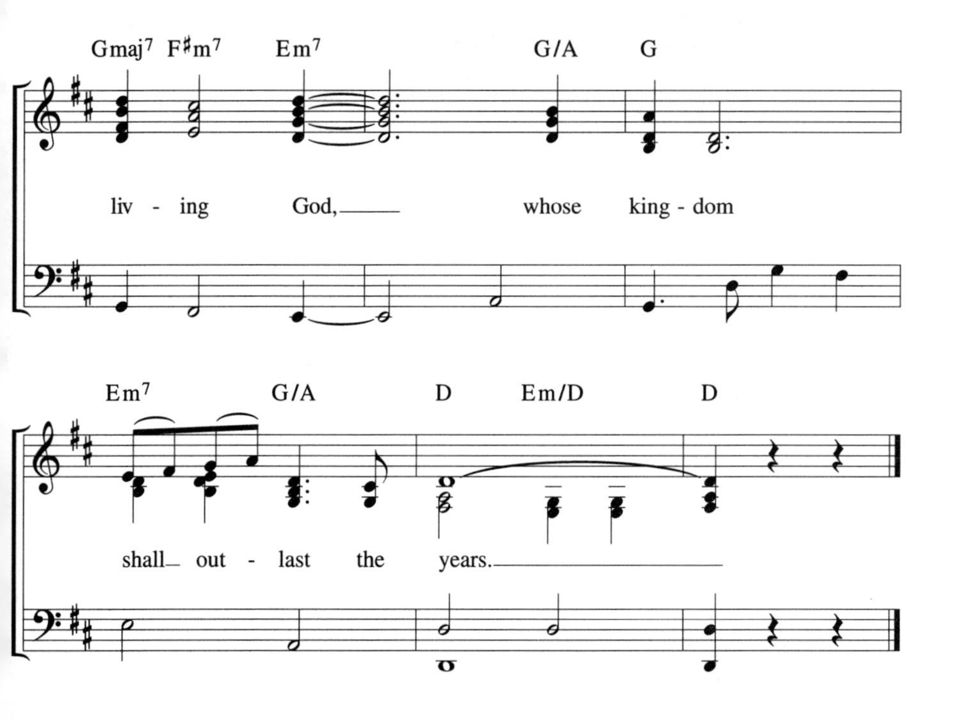

Verse 2:
Restore, O Lord
In all the earth Your fame
And in our time revive
The church that bears Your name.
And in Your anger
Lord, remember mercy
O living God
Whose mercy shall outlast the years.

Verse 3:
Bend us, O Lord
Where we are hard and cold
In Your refiner's fire
Come purify the gold.
Though suff'ring comes
And evil crouches near
Still our living God
Is reigning, He is reigning here.

Verse 4: (as verse 1)

Salvation Belongs To Our God

Adrian Howard / Pat Turner

Verse 2:
And we, the redeemed, shall be strong
In purpose and unity
Declaring aloud
Praise and glory, wisdom and thanks
Honour and power and strength.

Seek Ye First

Karen Lafferty

Verse 2:
You shall not live by bread alone
But by ev'ry word
That proceeds from the mouth of God
Hallelu, hallelujah!

Verse 3:
Ask and it shall be given unto you
Seek and you shall find
Knock and it shall be opened unto you
Hallelu, hallelujah!

Verse 4:
If the Son shall set you free
You shall be free indeed
You shall know the truth
and the truth shall set you free
Hallelu, hallelujah!

Verse 5:
Let your light so shine before men
That they may see your good works
And glorify your Father in heaven
Hallelu, hallelujah!

Verse 6:
Trust in the Lord with all your heart
He shall direct your paths
In all your ways acknowledge Him
Hallelu, hallelujah!

Soften My Heart, Lord

Graham Kendrick

Spirit Of The Living God

Daniel Iverson

Such Love

Graham Kendrick

Verse 2:
Such love, stilling my restlessness
Such love, filling my emptiness
Such love, showing me holiness
O Jesus, such love.

Verse 3:
Such love, springs from eternity
Such love, streaming through history
Such love, fountain of life to me
O Jesus, such love.

Tell Out, My Soul

Walter Greatorex / Timothy Dudley-Smith

Verse 2:
Tell out, my soul
The greatness of His name
Make known His might
The deeds His arm has done
His mercy sure
From age to age the same
His holy name;
The Lord, the Mighty One.

Verse 3:
Tell out, my soul
The greatness of His might
Pow'rs and dominions
Lay their glory by
Proud hearts and stubborn wills
Are put to flight
The hungry fed
The humble lifted high.

Verse 4:
Tell out, my soul
The glories of His word
Firm is His promise
And His mercy sure.
Tell out, my soul
The greatness of the Lord
To children's children
And for evermore.

Thank You For Saving Me

Martin Smith

B/D♯
A/C♯
A
B7sus4
You took my sin and shame, a sin - ner called by
E
Chorus
A add 9
name.
Great
E
B sus4
B
is the Lord.
A add 9
E
B sus4
Great is the Lord.
B
C♯m7
A
E
A
For we know Your truth has set us

Verse 2:
Mercy and grace are mine, forgiv'n is my sin
Jesus, my only hope, the Saviour of the world.
'Great is the Lord,' we cry; God, let Your kingdom come.
Your word has let me see, thank You for saving me.

There Is Power In The Name Of Jesus

Noel Richards

D
F
we are saved!
We are saved!
G
Am
At His name
Em7
F
the de - mons flee.
G
Am
Em7
At His name
cap - tives are freed,
F
G
F
for there is no oth - er name

G
Am
D
that is high - - - er
F
Gsus4
G
than Je - - - - - - - - sus!
C
F
1.
2.
Gsus4
G
Gsus4
G
C
2. There is pow'r
Verse 2:
There is pow'r in the name of Jesus
Like a sword in our hands.
We declare in the name of Jesus
We shall stand! We shall stand!
At His name God's enemies
Shall be crushed beneath our feet
For there is no other name that is higher
Than Jesus!

The Crucible For Silver

Martin Smith

Chorus
F
B♭add9
Gm7
Gm7/F
Je - sus, Ho-ly One, You are my heart's de - sire.
C
F
B♭
King of kings, my ev-'ry - thing, You've
Gm7
Gm7/F
1.
C
2.
C
set this heart on fire.
F
Fa-ther, take our of - fer-ing, with our

B♭
song we hum - bly praise You. You have brought Your ho - ly fi - re to our

Gm7
F
lips.
Stand-ing in Your beau - ty, Lord, Your

B♭
gift to us is ho - li-ness; lead us to the place where we can

Gm
B♭
sing:

F
B♭add9
Gm7
Gm7/F
Chorus
Je - sus, Ho-ly One You are my heart's de - sire.

C
F
King of kings, my

B♭
Gm7
Gm7/F
ev - 'ry - thing, You've set this heart on fire.

C
F

The King Is Among Us

Graham Kendrick

Verse 2:
He looks down upon us
Delight in His face
Enjoying His children's love
Enthralled by our praise.

Verse 3:
For each child is special
Accepted and loved
A love gift from Jesus
To His Father above.

Verse 4:
And now He is giving
His gifts to us all
For no one is worthless
And each one is called.

Verse 5:
The Spirit's anointing
On all flesh comes down
And we shall be channels
For works like His own.

Verse 6:
We come now believing
Your promise of power
For we are Your people
And this is Your hour.

Verse 7:
As verse 1

There Is A Redeemer

Melody Green

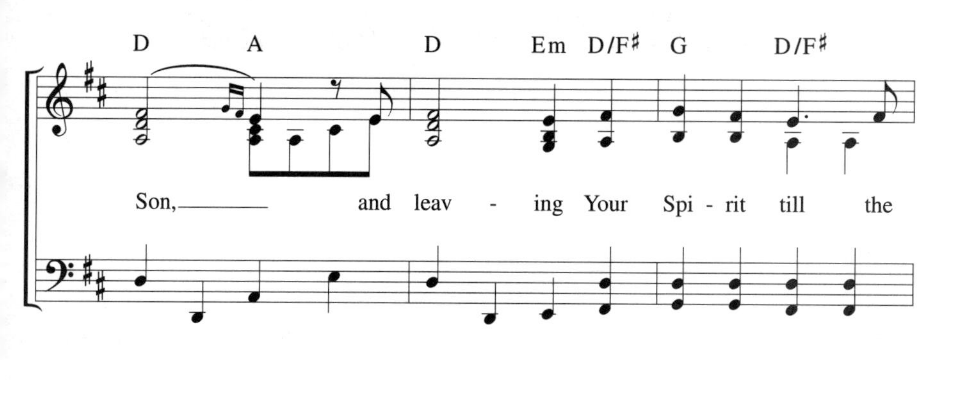

Verse 2:
Jesus, my Redeemer
Name above all names
Precious Lamb of God, Messiah
O for sinners slain.

Verse 3:
When I stand in glory
I will see His face.
And there I'll serve my King for ever
In that Holy Place.

There's A Quiet Understanding

Tedd Smith

Verse 2:
And we know when we're together
Sharing love and understanding
That our brothers and our sisters
Feel the oneness that He brings.
Thank You, thank You, thank You, Jesus
For the way You love and feed us
For the many ways You lead us
Thank You, thank You, Lord.

These Are The Days Of Elijah

(Days Of Elijah)

Robin Mark

D/A
A/E
E
these are the days of your servant, Mo-ses, right-eous-ness be-ing re-
A
C♯m
F♯m
-stored. And though these are days of great tri-al, of
Bm7
Bm7/A
E
fa-mine and dark-ness and sword, still
A
D/A
we are the voice in the de-sert cry-ing, 'Pre-
A/E
E
A
Chorus
-pare ye the way of the Lord.' Be-hold, He

Verse 2:
These are the days of Ezekiel
The dry bones becoming as flesh
And these are the days of Your servant, David
Rebuilding a temple of praise.
These are the days of the harvest
The fields are as white in the world
And we are the lab'rers in Your vineyard
Declaring the work of the Lord.

To Be In Your Presence

(My Desire)

Noel Richards

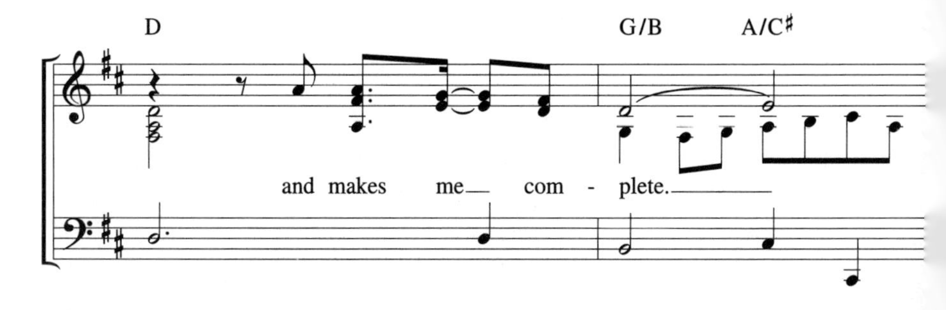

Verse 2:
To rest in your presence, not rushing away
To cherish each moment, here I would stay.

To You, O Lord

Graham Kendrick

Chorus
F
C/F
B♭/F
C7sus4
No one whose hope is in You will ev-er be put to shame;
F
C/F
B♭
Csus4
C
that's why my eyes are on You, O Lord.
Dm
Dm/C
Dm/B
Sur-round me, de-fend me, O how I need You.
B♭
Gm7
To You I lift up my soul, to You I lift up my soul.
B♭/C
C
F
C/F
B♭/F
F

1.
2, 𝄋.
To Coda
C/F
B♭/F
B♭/F
Verse
F
C/F
B♭/F
F
3. Re-mem-ber, Lord, Your mer-cy and love
C/F
B♭
F
that ev-er flow from of old.
C/F
B♭/F
Am/F
F
Re-mem-ber not the sins of my youth
C
B♭add9
or my re-bel-li-ous ways.
Ac-cord-ing to You

Verse 2:
Show me Your ways and teach me Your paths
Guide me in truth, lead me on
For You're my God, You are my Saviour
My hope is in You each moment of the day.

We Are Marching

From "Freedom Is Coming" (Wild Goose Publications 1990).
Original Xhosa text & melody South African traditional.

Verse 2:
We are living in the love of God…

Verse 3:
We are moving in the pow'r of God…

We Believe

Graham Kendrick

A
Then from death He rose vic - to - rious, as -
F♯m
E
- cen - ded to the Fa - ther's side.
F♯m
E
F♯m
Je - - - - sus. Lord of all,
E
A
Lord of all, Je - - - - sus, Lord of
1.
2.
F♯m
E
all, Lord of all, Lord of

Verse 2:
We believe He sends His Spirit
On His church with gifts of pow'r.
God, His word of truth affirming
Send us to the nations now.
He will come again in glory
Judge the living and the dead.
Ev'ry knee shall bow before Him
Then must ev'ry tongue confess.

We Want To See Jesus Lifted High

Doug Horley

G
D
Em
C
We want to see,
(We're gon-na)
we want to see,
(we're gon-na)
we want to see Je -
(we're gon-na)

G
D
To Coda
- sus lift - ed high.
We want to see,
(We're gon - na)
we want to see,
(we're gon-na)

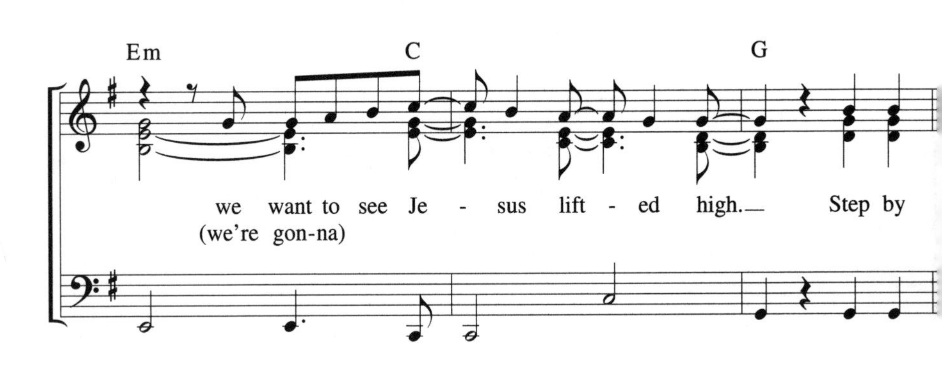
Em
C
G
we want to see Je - sus lift - ed high.
(we're gon-na)
Step by

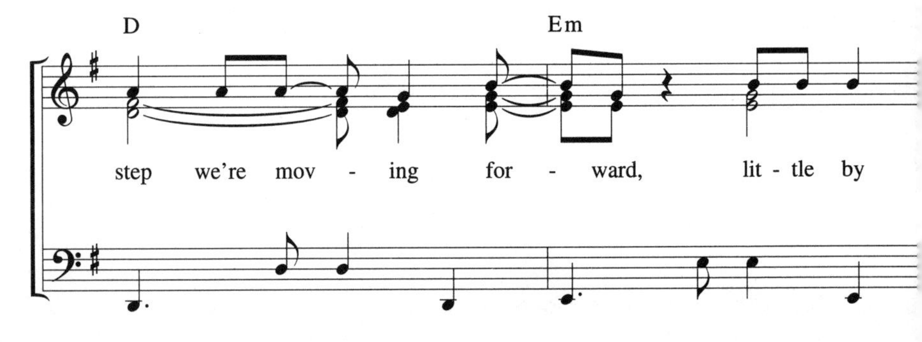
D
Em
step we're mov - ing for - ward, lit - tle by

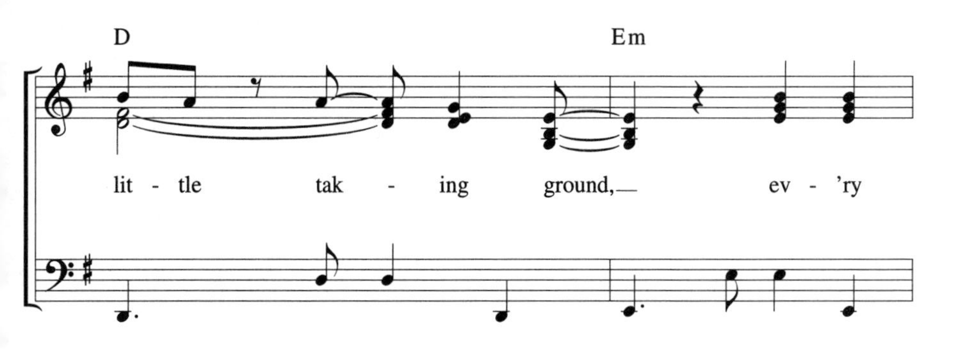
D
Em
lit - tle tak - ing ground,_ ev - 'ry

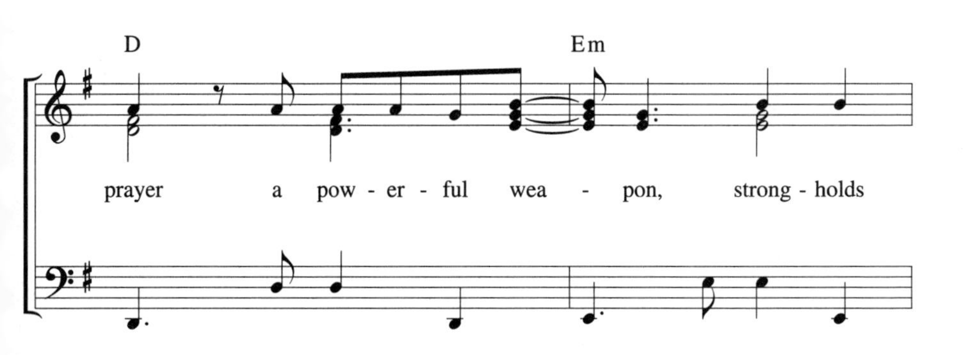
D
Em
prayer a pow - er - ful wea - pon, strong - holds

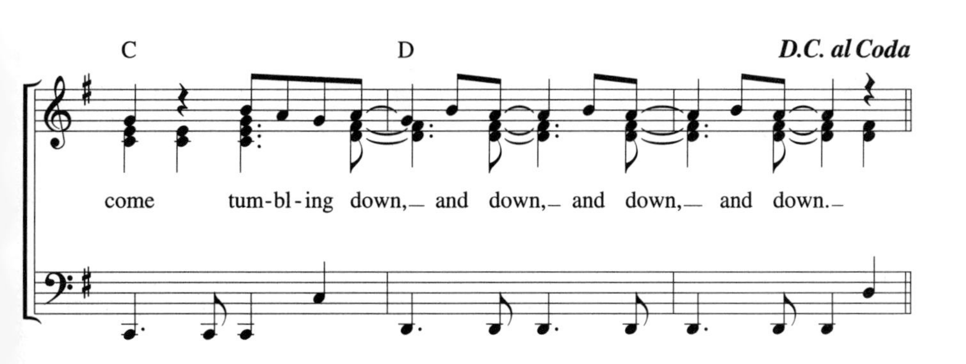
C
D
D.C. al Coda
come tum-bl-ing down,_ and down,_ and down,_ and down._

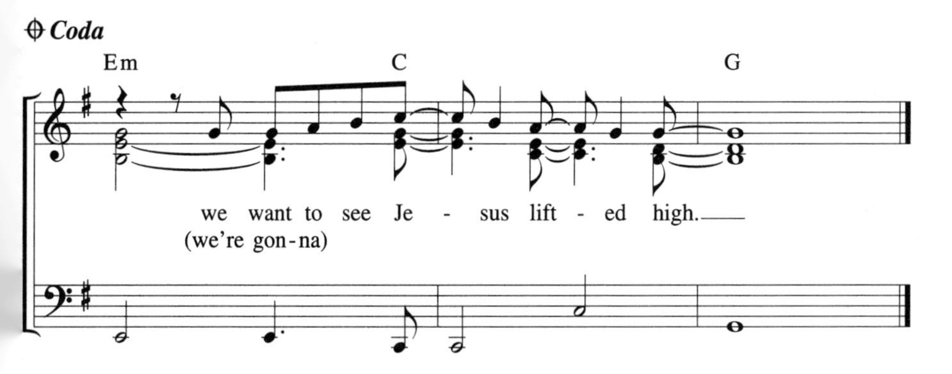
Coda
Em
C
G
we want to see Je - sus lift - ed high.___
(we're gon-na)

What A Friend I've Found

(Jesus, Friend Forever)

Martin Smith

Verse 2:
What a hope I've found
More faithful than a mother.
It would break my heart
To ever lose each other.

When I Feel The Touch

David Matthew / Keri Jones

What Kind Of Love Is This

Bryn Haworth / Sally Haworth

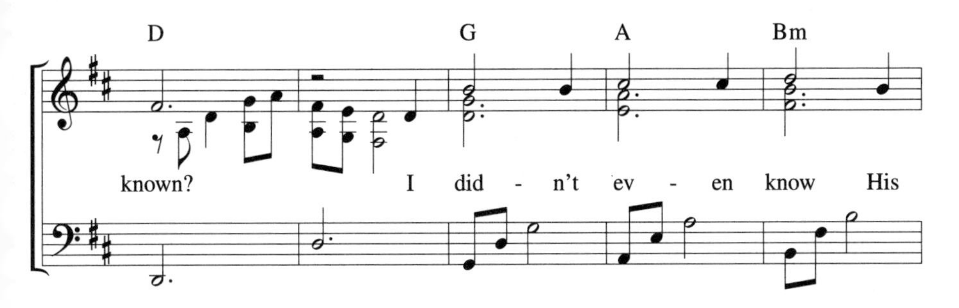

Verse 2:
What kind of man is this
That died in agony?
He who had done no wrong
Was crucified for me.
What kind of man is this
Who laid aside His thrine
That I may know the love of God?
What kind of man is this?

Verse 3:
By grace I have been saved
It is the gift of God
He destined me to be His child
Such is His love.
No eye has ever seen
No ear has ever heard
Nor has the heart of man conceived
What kind of love is this.

When I Look Into Your Holiness

Cathy Perrin / Wayne Perrin

Dm Dm7 G Gsus4 G
3
shadows in the light of You: I worship
F G Em Am
3
You, I worship You, the
Dm G7 C G/C C
3 3
reason I live is to worship You. I worship
F G Em Am
3
You, I worship You, the
Dm G7 C F/C C
3
reason I live is to worship You

When The Music Fades

(The Heart Of Worship)

Matt Redman

F♯m7 E/G♯ B
I'll bring You more than a song, for a song in it - self
F♯m7 E/G♯ B
is not what You have re - quired.
F♯m7 E/G♯ B
You search much deep - er with - in, through the way things ap - pear;
F♯m7 E/G♯ B
You're look - ing in - to my heart.
E Chorus B/D♯
I'm com - ing back to the heart of wor - ship, and it's

Verse 2:
King of endless worth
No one could express
How much You deserve.
Though I'm weak and poor
All I have is Yours
Ev'ry single breath.

You're The Lion Of Judah

(Lion Of Judah)

Robin Mark

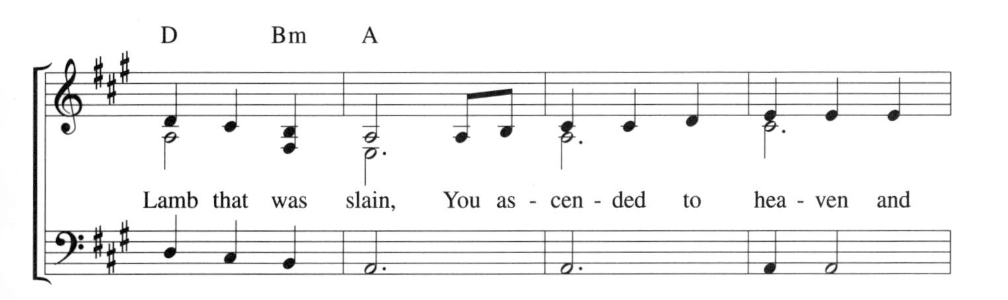

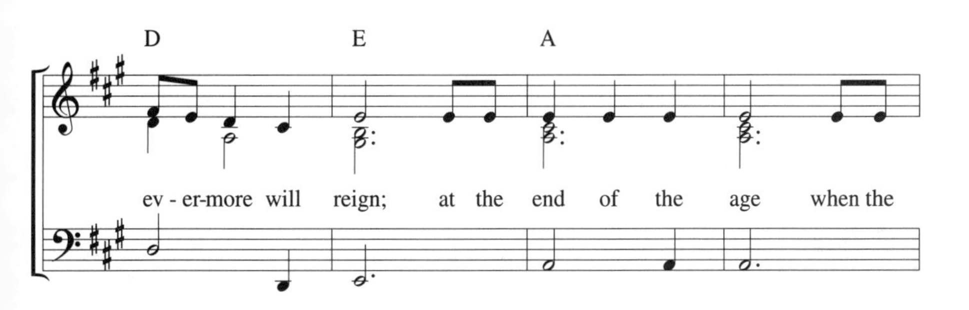

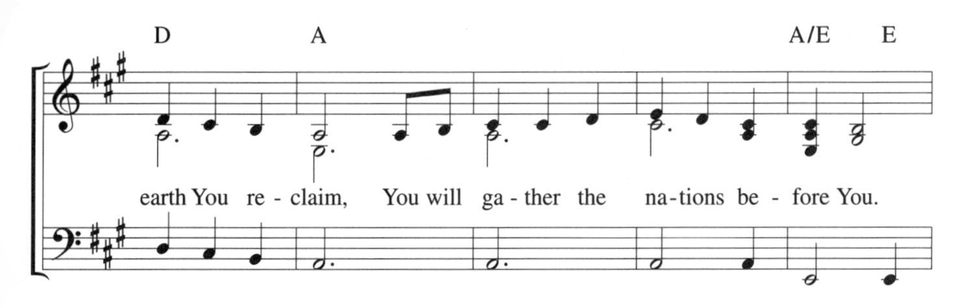

And the eyes of all men will be fixed on the Lamb who was
D
E
cru - - ci - - fied, for with wis-dom and
mer-cy and jus-tice He reigns at the
D
Fa - - ther's
E
Chorus
A
D
side. And the an-gels will cry: 'Hail
A
E
the Lamb who was

Verse 2:
There's a shield in our hand and a sword at our side
There's a fire in our spirit that cannot be denied
As the Father has told us, for these You have died
For the nations that gather before You.
And the ears of all men
Need to hear of the Lamb who was crucified
Who descended to hell
Yet was raised up to reign at the Father's side.

Who Has Laid The Earth's Foundations

(Lord Of Hosts)

Johnny Markin

Verse 2:
Who has sealed the ocean's boundaries
So contained its raging power?
When the word went forth from heaven's glory
The fountains of the deep were held at bay!

Verse 3:
Who commands the light of morning
Caused the dawn to know its place
As the darkness flees His holy presence
And evil men take flight from His glorious grace?

You Are Beautiful

(I Stand In Awe)

Mark Altrogge

D E A
fa-thom the depth of Your love? You are beau-ti-ful be-yond de-scrip-
E/A D Esus4 A Esus4 E
-tion, Ma-jes-ty, en-throned a-bove. And I
A E/A D
stand, I stand in awe of you. I
A E/A D G♯7sus4 C♯7
stand, I stand in awe of you. Ho-ly God, to whom all
D F♯m/D♯ Bm7 E D/A A
praise is due, I stand in awe of You.

You Laid Aside Your Majesty

(I Really Want To Worship You, My Lord)

Noel Richards

G D Em Bm
I real-ly want to wor-ship You, my Lord, You have won my heart and I am
C A7 Am7 D
yours for ev-er and ev-er; I will love You.
G D Em
You are the on-ly one who died for me, gave Your life
Bm C A7 Am7
to set me free, so I lift my voice to You in a-do-
D G C Dsus4 D G
-ra - - - - tion.

Index of titles

If a song is also known by an alternative title, this is shown by the use of *italics*.